Contents

How to use this book

The contents of this study and revision guide are designed to guide you through to success in the Mechanics M1 component of the WJEC Mathematics AS level examination. It has been written by an experienced author and teacher and edited by a senior subject expert. This book has been written specifically for the WJEC AS course you are taking and includes everything you need to know to perform well in your exams.

Knowledge and Understanding

Topics start with a short list of the material covered in the topic and each topic will give the underpinning knowledge and skills you need to perform well in your exams.

If any formulae are included in a topic, you will be told whether you need to remember them or whether they will be given in the formula booklet.

Formulae used will be highlighted and will be included in a Topic summary at the end of each topic.

The knowledge section is kept fairly short, leaving plenty of space for detailed explanation of examples. Pointers will be given to the theory, examples and questions that will help you understand the thinking behind the steps. You will also be given detailed advice when it is needed.

Grade boosts are tips to help you achieve your best grade by avoiding certain pitfalls which can let students down.

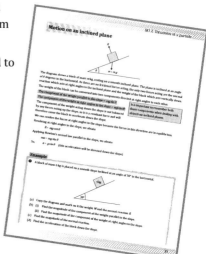

Exam Practice and Technique

Helping you understand how to answer examination questions lies at the heart of this book. This means that we have included questions throughout the book that will build up your skills and knowledge until you are at a stage to answer full exam questions on your own. Examples are included; some of which are based on recent examination questions. These are annotated with Pointers and general advice about the knowledge, skills and techniques needed to answer them. There is a comprehensive Q&A section in each topic that provides actual examination questions with commentary so you can see how the question should be answered.

There is a Test yourself section where you are encouraged to answer questions on the topic and then compare your answers with the ones given at the back of the book. You should of course work through complete examination papers as part of your revision process.

We advise that you look at the WJEC website *www.wjec.co.uk* where you can download materials such as the specification and past papers to help you with your studies. From this website you will be able to download the formula booklet that you will use in your examinations. You will also find specimen papers and mark schemes on the site.

Good luck with your revision.

Stephen Doyle

Howard Thomas

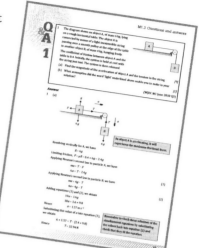

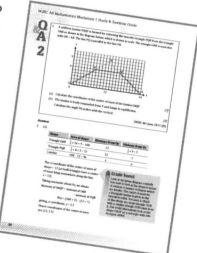

Unit M1 **Mechanics 1**

Unit M1 covers Mechanics and will involve some of the mathematics covered during your GCSE course. You must be proficient in the use of mathematical theories and techniques such as solving simple equations, transposing formulae, algebraic manipulation, solving simultaneous equations, etc., and this may require you looking back over you GCSE work.

The knowledge, skills and understanding of the material in M1 will be built on in the other optional mechanics units you may take.

Revision checklist

Tick column 1 when you have completed all the notes.
Tick column 2 when you think you have a good grasp of the topic.
Tick column 3 during the final revision when you feel you have mastery of the topic.

Unit M1 Mechanics 1			1	2	3	Notes
Topic 1 **Rectilinear motion**	p8	Motion under uniform acceleration				
	p9	Velocity–time graphs				
	p13	Vertical motion under gravity				
	p15	Sketching and interpretation of velocity–time graphs				
Topic 2 **Dynamics of a particle**	p24	Newton's laws of motion				
	p25	Types of force				
	p27	Lifts accelerating, decelerating and travelling with constant velocity				
	p31	Motion on an inclined plane				
	p32	The motion of particles connected by strings passing over fixed pulleys or pegs				
Topic 3 **Friction**	p43	Friction				
	p43	Laws of friction				
	p44	Limiting friction and the coefficient of friction				
Topic 4 **Momentum and impulse**	p54	Momentum and impulse				
	p55	Conservation of momentum				
	p55	Newton's experimental law for the direct impact of two bodies moving in the same straight line				
	p57	Newton's experimental law for the impact of a body moving at right angles to a plane				

Topic 1 〉 Rectilinear motion

This topic covers the following:

- Motion under uniform acceleration
- Vertical motion under gravity

Motion under uniform acceleration

This topic looks at motion under uniform acceleration. Uniform acceleration means motion with constant acceleration in either the horizontal or vertical direction.

Some important definitions of terms used

The following terms are used to describe motion and you need to understand their meanings:

Distance – this is the length that is travelled and is measured in metres (m). If you walked in a straight line from A to B and then back to A, then the distance travelled would be twice the distance from A to B. Distance is a scalar quantity because it has size only.

Displacement – is a vector quantity which means it has both magnitude (i.e., size) and direction. Displacement can therefore be positive or negative. For example, if you walked in a straight line from A to B and then back to A, the displacement would be zero. This is because the displacement one way would be positive and the displacement in the opposite direction would be negative. Displacement is measured in metres (m).

Speed – is a scalar quantity so it has no direction. If the speed is uniform, then speed is the distance travelled divided by the time taken (i.e., the rate of change of distance with time) and is measured in metres per second ($m\,s^{-1}$).

Velocity – is a vector quantity so it has both size and direction. If the velocity is uniform, then velocity is the change in displacement divided by the time taken (i.e., the rate of change of displacement with time) and is measured in metres per second ($m\,s^{-1}$).

Acceleration – is a vector quantity and is the change in velocity divided by the time taken. It is measured in metres per second squared ($m\,s^{-2}$).

Velocity–time graphs for motion under uniform acceleration

The main features of a velocity–time graph are:

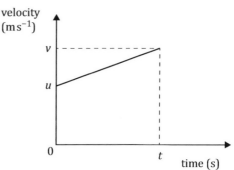

- The gradient represents the acceleration. From the graph $a = \dfrac{v - u}{t}$. A negative gradient represents a deceleration.
- The area under the line represents the distance travelled or displacement. From the graph, distance travelled/ displacement = area under the graph (i.e., the area of the trapezium) = $\frac{1}{2}(u + v)t$. If the area is under the time axis, this area represents a negative displacement.

Area of trapezium = $\frac{1}{2}$(sum of the two parallel sides) × perpendicular distance between them.

- Horizontal lines (i.e., parallel to the time axis) represent constant velocity.

The following graph represents a journey:

The gradient of line OA represents the acceleration.

Line AB represents travelling at constant velocity.

The gradient of line BC represents the acceleration. Because the gradient is negative, the acceleration will be negative showing a deceleration.

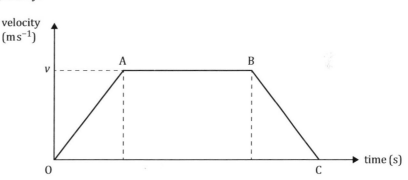

Examples

❶ The velocity–time graph shown below represents the four stages of motion of a vehicle moving along a straight horizontal road. The initial velocity of the vehicle is 20 m s^{-1}.

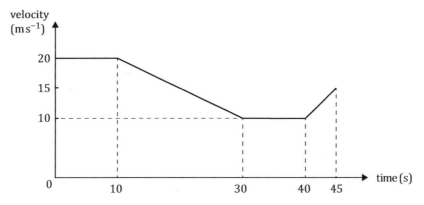

(a) Find the distance travelled whilst the car is decelerating.

(b) Find the total distance travelled whilst travelling at constant speed.

(c) During the later stage of the motion the car accelerates. Calculate the magnitude of the acceleration.

(d) Calculate the total distance travelled during the motion described by the graph.

Answer

Area of trapezium = $\frac{1}{2}$(sum of the two parallel sides) × perpendicular distance between them. You could alternatively, divide the shape into a triangle and a rectangle and add the two areas together. Note you will not be given the formula for the area of a trapezium in the formula booklet.

① (a) Distance = Area of trapezium = $\frac{1}{2}\left(20 + 10\right) \times 20$

$$= 300 \, \text{m}$$

(b) Total distance whilst travelling at constant speed

$$= (20 \times 10) + (10 \times 10) = 300 \, \text{m}$$

(c) Acceleration = Gradient = $\dfrac{15 - 10}{5} = 1 \, \text{m s}^{-2}$

(d) Distance travelled whilst accelerating $= \frac{1}{2}\left(10 + 15\right) \times 5$

$$= 62.5 \, \text{m}$$

Total distance travelled = 300 + 300 + 62.5 = 662.5 m

❷ Cars A and B are travelling a long straight road. At time $t = 0$ Car A is travelling with a speed of 20 m s⁻¹ and at this time it overtakes Car B travelling with a speed of 15 m s⁻¹. Car B immediately accelerates uniformly and both cars travel a distance of 600 m before Cars A and B are level and overtake each other again.

(a) Draw a velocity–time graph showing the motion of the cars from where they are first level to when they are level again.

(b) Show that the time between overtaking the first and second time is 30 s.

(c) Calculate the magnitude of the velocity of Car B after 30 s.

(d) Calculate the acceleration of Car B.

Answer

② (a)

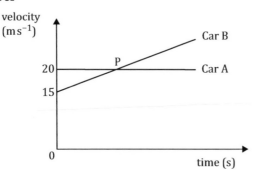

Note that the point P relates to Car B's velocity being equal to Car A's velocity not where Car B overtakes Car A.

(b) Considering the motion of Car A, suppose the cars are level after time t.

The area under the velocity–time graph for Car A = 600.

Hence $20 \times t = 600$

giving $t = 30 \, \text{s}$

This is the area under the graph, which is a rectangle of length 20 and width t.

(c) After 30 s the distance travelled by Car B is 600 m.

Let the velocity of Car B after 30 s = v

Area under the graph = area of a trapezium = $\frac{1}{2}(15 + v) \times 30$

Now, distance travelled = area under the graph

Hence $600 = \frac{1}{2}(15 + v) \times 30$

Solving this equation gives $v = 25$ m s^{-1}

(d)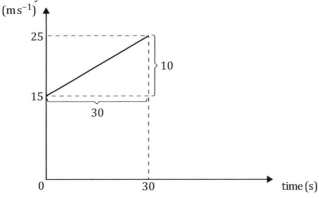

Acceleration = Gradient = $\dfrac{10}{30} = 0.33$ m s^{-2}

Motion under uniform acceleration

Rectilinear motion is motion in a straight line. In this section you will be looking at a set of equations that connect quantities such as velocities, distances/displacements, time and accelerations for motion under uniform acceleration. Uniform acceleration means that the acceleration remains at a constant value during the section of the motion being considered.

If a body is uniformly accelerated in a straight line, then the following equations, called the equations of motion (or *suvat* equations), can be used. The meaning of the terms used in the equations is shown in the table:

Equations	Terms
$v = u + at$	s = displacement/distance
$s = ut + \frac{1}{2}at^2$	u = initial velocity
$v^2 = u^2 + 2as$	v = final velocity
$s = \frac{1}{2}(u + v)t$	a = acceleration
	t = time

Important note

You need to remember all the equations above as they will not be given in the formula booklet.

Notice that there are four variables in each equation, so you would need to know three of them in order to find the value of the fourth variable.

Displacement, initial velocity, final velocity and acceleration are all vector quantities, which means they have both a magnitude (i.e., size) and a direction.

Normally the direction is taken as positive from left to right, so for example, a ball moving from right to left would have a negative velocity.

Example

① A car is travelling along a straight road ABC with uniform acceleration a m s^{-2}. The distance AB is 95 m. The time taken by the car to travel from A to B is 5 s and the time taken to travel from B to C is 2 s. At A the speed of the car is u m s^{-1} and, at C, its speed is 29.8 m s^{-1}. Find the value of a and the value of u.   *[7]*

(WJEC M1 June 2010 Q8)

Answer

①

For the journey from A to C we have

$v = 29.8$, $t = 5 + 2 = 7$

Hence using $v = u + at$ gives

$$29.8 = u + 7a \qquad (1)$$

For the journey from A to B we have

$s = 95$, $t = 5$

Hence using $s = ut + \frac{1}{2}at^2$ gives

$$95 = 5u + 12.5a \qquad (2)$$

Solving equations (1) and (2) simultaneously, we obtain

Acceleration, $a = 2.4$ m s^{-2} and initial velocity, $u = 13$ m s^{-1}

> You need to consider two journeys; one from A to C and the other from A to B. If you considered a journey from B to C you would need to introduce another variable for velocity at B which would complicate things because there would now be three unknowns.

> Many of the questions in this topic involve the creation of two equations involving two unknowns which need to be solved simultaneously. Make sure you can solve simultaneous equations and check the answers you obtain.

Vertical motion under gravity

Particles travelling in a vertical direction experience a constant acceleration of 9.8 m s^{-2} acting towards the centre of the earth. When travelling upwards, this acceleration opposes the motion and is -9.8 m s^{-2}. When travelling downwards, this acceleration accelerates the particle and is taken as 9.8 m s^{-2}. As velocities and accelerations can act in different directions, you have to decide which direction you intend to take as the positive direction.

Remember to say which direction you are taking as positive in your answer.

Examples

❶ A ball is thrown vertically down a well with an initial velocity of 5 m s^{-1}. The ball takes 6 seconds to reach the bottom of the well.

(a) Find the velocity of the ball after 6 seconds.

(b) Find the distance travelled by the ball when it reaches the bottom of the well.

Answer

① (a) Taking downwards as the positive direction, we have

$u = 5, a = g = 9.8, t = 6, v = ?$

Using $v = u + at$

$v = 5 + (9.8 \times 6) = 63.8$ m s^{-1}

(b) Using $s = ut + \frac{1}{2}at^2$ we have

$s = (5 \times 6) + \left(\frac{1}{2} \times 9.8 \times 6^2\right) = 206.4$ m

> Write down all the letters with values that are known and also write the letter of the quantity you wish to find with a question mark.
>
> Then you need to choose the equation from the list. It is a good idea to write down the list at the start as it will help you to remember them.

❷ A ball is thrown vertically upwards with an initial velocity of 10 m s^{-1}.

(a) Find the maximum height reached by the ball.

(b) Find the time taken for the ball to reach its maximum height.

Answer

② (a) Taking upwards as the positive direction, we have

$u = 10, v = 0, a = -g = -9.8, s = ?$

Using $v^2 = u^2 + 2as$, we obtain

$0^2 = 10^2 + (2 \times (-9.8) \times s)$

giving $s = 5.10$ m.

(b) Using $v = u + at$, we obtain $0 = 10 + (-9.8)t$, giving $t = 1.02$ s

> When the ball reaches its maximum height, its velocity is zero.

> If upwards is taken as positive, then g is acting in the opposite direction so it has a negative value (i.e. -9.8).

❸ A stone is thrown vertically **downwards** from the top of a cliff with an initial velocity of 1 m s^{-1} and hits the sea 2.5 seconds later.

(a) Find the speed with which the stone hits the sea. [3]

(b) Calculate the height of the cliff. [3]

(WJEC M1 June 2011 Q1)

Answer

③ (a) Taking downwards as the positive direction, we have

$u = 1, t = 2.5, a = g = 9.8, v = ?$

Using $v = u + at$ we have, $v = 1 + (9.8 \times 2.5) = 25.5 \text{ m s}^{-1}$

(b) Using $s = ut + \frac{1}{2}at^2 = (1 \times 2.5) + \left(\frac{1}{2} \times 9.8 \times 2.5^2\right) = 33.125 \text{ m}$

❹ A stone is thrown vertically upwards with a speed of 14.7 m s^{-1} from a point A which is 49 m above the ground.

(a) Find the time taken for the stone to reach the ground. [3]

(b) Calculate the speed of the stone when it hits the ground. [3]

(WJEC M1 Jan 2012 Q4)

Answer

④ (a) Taking upwards as the positive direction, we have

$u = 14.7, s = -49, a = -g = -9.8, t = ?$

Using $s = ut + \frac{1}{2}at^2$ we obtain

$-49 = 14.7t + \left(\frac{1}{2} \times (-9.8)t^2\right)$

$-49 = 14.7t - 4.9\,t^2$

$0 = 4.9\,t^2 - 14.7t - 49$

$0 = t^2 - 3t - 10$

$0 = (t - 5)(t + 2)$

Giving $t = 5, -2$ (you cannot have a negative time so $t = -2$ is ignored)

Hence time taken = 5 s

> Notice we use $s = -49$. This is because the displacement is 49 m below the point of projection and therefore represents a negative displacement.

> It looks as though you may need to use the quadratic formula to solve this quadratic equation. However, it is always worth checking to see if the coefficient of x^2 (4.9 in this case) divides exactly into the other numbers. On doing this here, you end up with a quadratic that can be easily factorised.

(b) Using $v = u + at$, we have

$v = 14.7 + (-9.8 \times 5) = -34.3 \text{ m s}^{-1}$

Hence   speed = 34.3 m s^{-1}

> The negative sign tells us that this velocity is downwards (i.e. opposite to the direction of the initial velocity).

> Speed is a scalar quantity so it only has size. We therefore remove the negative sign.

Sketching and interpretation of velocity–time graphs

Sketching velocity–time graphs

In some examination questions you will be asked to draw a velocity–time graph for motion described in a question. In some cases you will need to add some information, which you will need to calculate first in order to draw your graph.

Example

❶ A car is travelling along a straight horizontal road. There are three stages to its motion.

During the first stage of the motion, it accelerates uniformly from rest with an acceleration of 1 m s^{-2} for 10 s.

During the second stage of the motion, the car travels at constant velocity for 15 s.

During the third stage of the motion, the car decelerates uniformly to rest in 5 s.

(a) Show that the velocity reached after the first stage of the motion is 10 m s^{-1}.

(b) Find the deceleration during the third stage of the motion.

(c) Sketch a velocity–time graph that shows the three stages of the motion.

(d) Calculate the total distance travelled during the three stages of motion.

Answer

① (a) $u = 0, a = 1, t = 10, v = ?$

Using $v = u + at$

$\qquad v = 0 + (1 \times 10) = 10 \text{ m s}^{-1}$

(b) $u = 0, v = 0, t = 5, a = ?$

Using $v = u + at$

$\qquad 0 = 10 + 5a$

$\qquad a = -2 \text{ m s}^{-2}$ (note that a negative acceleration is a deceleration)

Hence deceleration $= 2 \text{ m s}^{-2}$

(c)

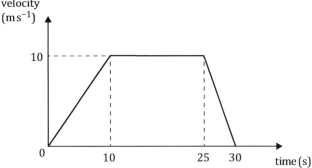

(d) Total distance travelled = Area under the velocity–time graph

$$= \tfrac{1}{2}(30 + 15) \times 10 = 225 \text{ m}$$

> The formula for the area of a trapezium is used here which you will need to remember. Or you could find the combined areas of 2 triangles and a rectangle.

Interpretation of velocity–time graphs

The diagram below shows a velocity–time graph. You must be able to interpret the graph and describe the motion it represents.

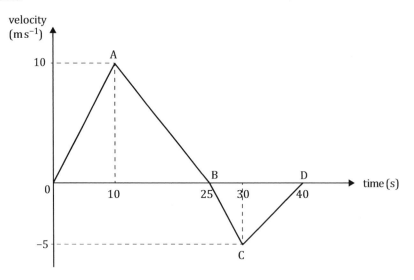

The graph has been divided into sections.

OA represents acceleration from 0 to 10 m s^{-1}.

Acceleration = the gradient of line OA = $\frac{10}{10}$ = 1 m s^{-2}.

AB represents a negative acceleration. The acceleration = $-\frac{10}{15}$ = -0.67 m s^{-2}. Note that the negative sign can be removed if it is described as a deceleration.

BC represents an acceleration, but this time because the velocity is negative, it means that the motion is in the opposite direction. The acceleration = $\frac{-5}{5}$ = -1 m s^{-2}. Notice that because the negative acceleration is in the same direction as the velocity, it represents an acceleration rather than a deceleration.

The displacement from 0 to B is the area under the velocity–time graph between 0 and B.

Area = Area of a triangle = $\frac{1}{2}$ × base × height = $\frac{1}{2}$ × 25 × 10 = 125 m

The displacement from B to D = $\frac{1}{2}$ × 15 × 5 = -37.5 m. Note that because the area lies under the time axis, it represents a negative displacement. This means that the object is moving back in the opposite direction so it is now moving nearer to 0.

The displacement from 0 to D = 125 – 37.5 = 87.5 m

The total distance travelled from 0 to D = 125 + 37.5 = 162.5 m

Example

❶ A particle starting from rest and travelling in a straight line, accelerates uniformly for 2 s and reaches a constant velocity of u m s^{-1}. It then travels at constant velocity for 10 s, before decelerating uniformly to rest in 3 s. The total distance travelled by the particle was 50 m.

(a) Draw a velocity–time graph to show the motion of the particle.

(b) Find the value of u.

(c) Find the magnitude of the deceleration.

Answer

① (a)

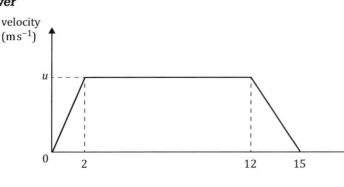

> When drawing a velocity–time graph, ensure that the axes are labelled with quantities and units.
>
> Put any values and letters for quantities which need to be found, on the graph.

(b) Total distance travelled = Area under the velocity–time graph

$$= \tfrac{1}{2}(15 + 10) \times u$$

> The formula for the area of a trapezium is used here.

But the total distance travelled = 50 m

Hence $\qquad 50 = \tfrac{1}{2}(15 + 10) \times u$, so $u = 4$ m s^{-1}

(c) Deceleration $= \tfrac{4}{3} = 1.33$ m s^{-2}

Examination style questions

① A lorry travels along a straight road from point A to point B. The lorry starts from rest and accelerates uniformly for 25 s until it reaches a steady speed of 20 m s⁻¹. It travels at this steady speed for T s until it starts to decelerate uniformly for 10 s until it reaches point B. It passes point B with a speed of 10 m s⁻¹ and the distance between points A and B is 12 km.

(a) Sketch a velocity–time graph for the journey between A and B.   [3]

(b) Find the total time for the journey from A to B.   [4]

Answer

① (a)

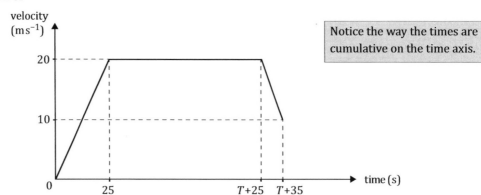

> Notice the way the times are cumulative on the time axis.

(b) Distance travelled = area under the velocity–time graph

= area of △ + area of ▢ + area of ▱

As distance travelled = 12 000 m,

we have $12\,000 = \left(\frac{1}{2} \times 25 \times 20\right) + (20 \times T) + \left(\frac{1}{2} \times (20 + 10) \times 10\right)$

$12\,000 = 250 + 20T + 150$

$12000 - 400 = 20T$

Giving $T = 580$ s

❷ A particle, moving in a straight line has its speed measured at points A and B. At point A, its speed is 20 m s⁻¹ and at point B its speed is 32 m s⁻¹. The distance between points A and B is 120 m.

(a) Show that the acceleration of the particle is 2.6 m s⁻². [3]

(b) Find the time for the particle to travel from A to B. [3]

(c) Find the speed of the particle 20 s after passing point A. [3]

(d) Calculate the distance from A 30 s after it passes A. [3]

(e) Sketch a velocity–time graph for the journey from A to B. [2]

Answer

② (a) $u = 20, v = 32, s = 120, a = ?$

Using $v^2 = u^2 + 2as,$

we obtain $32^2 = 20^2 + (2a \times 120)$

Solving gives $a = 2.6$ m s⁻²

(b) Using $v = u + at,$

we obtain $32 = 20 + 2.6t$

Solving, we obtain $t = 4.62$ s

(c) $u = 20, a = 2.6, t = 20, v = ?$

Using $v = u + at,$

we obtain $v = 20 + (2.6 \times 20)$

Solving, we obtain $v = 72$ m s⁻¹

(d) $u = 20, a = 2.6, t = 30, s = ?$

Using $s = ut + \frac{1}{2}at^2,$

we obtain $s = (20 \times 30) + \left(\frac{1}{2} \times 2.6 \times 30^2\right)$

$s = 1770$ m

(e)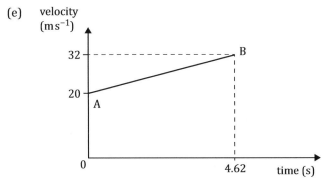

Test yourself

Answer the following questions and check your answers before moving on to the next topic.

1   A car starting from rest accelerates uniformly at 0.9 m s^{-2} for 5 seconds.

It then maintains a constant speed for 20 seconds before being uniformly decelerated for 8 seconds before coming to rest.

(a)   Sketch a velocity–time graph for the motion of the car.

(b)   Find the maximum velocity reached by the car.

(c)   Find the deceleration of the car.

(d)   Find the total distance travelled by the car.

2   A stone is projected vertically upwards with a velocity of 20 m s^{-1} from point A.

(a)   Calculate the greatest height from point A reached by the stone.

(b)   Calculate the time from when the stone is projected to when it returns to point A.

3   A stone is thrown vertically downwards from the top of a cliff with a velocity of 0.8 m s^{-1} and hits the sea 3.5 seconds later.

(a)   Calculate the speed with which the stone hits the sea.

(b)   Calculate the height of the cliff.

4   A particle is projected vertically upwards with a speed of 15 m s^{-1}.

(a)   Find the time in seconds for the particle to reach its greatest height.

(b)   Find the maximum height reached by the particle.

Q&A 1

1   A boy throws a ball vertically upwards from a point A with an initial speed of 18.2 m s^{-1}.

   (a)   Find the greatest height above A reached by the ball.   [3]

   (b)   Calculate the time taken for the ball to return to point A.   [3]

   (c)   Find the speed of the ball 2.5 s after it was thrown. State clearly the direction of motion of the ball at this time.   [3]

(WJEC M1 Jan 2010 Q1)

Answer

1   (a)   Taking the upward direction for the velocity as positive, we have

$u = 18.2$, $a = g = -9.8$, $v = 0$, $s = ?$

Using $v^2 = u^2 + 2as$ we have $0^2 = 18.2^2 + (2 \times (-9.8) \times s)$

Rearranging and solving we have $s = 16.9$ m

> Note that at the maximum height reached, the final velocity, v, is zero.

   (b)   Taking the upward direction for the velocity as positive, we have

$u = 18.2$, $a = g = -9.8$, $s = 0$, $t = ?$

$$s = ut + \tfrac{1}{2}at^2$$
$$0 = 18.2t + \left(\tfrac{1}{2} \times (-9.8) \times t^2\right)$$
$$0 = t(18.2 - 4.9t)$$

Solving gives $t = 0, 3.7$ s

Hence $t = 3.7$ s

> As the ball returns to its original starting point, the displacement is zero.

> $t = 0$ is ignored as this is the time when the ball first starts its journey. Hence $t = 3.7$ s.

   (c)   Taking the upward direction for the velocity as positive, we have

$u = 18.2$, $a = g = -9.8$, $t = 2.5$, $v = ?$

$v = u + at = 18.2 - (9.8 \times 2.5) = -6.3$ m s^{-1}

Hence the ball is moving downwards with a velocity of 6.3 m s^{-1}.

> As we have taken upward velocities as positive, the negative sign here means this velocity is downwards.

2 The points A, B and C lie, in that order, on a straight horizontal road. A car travels on the road with constant acceleration a m s^{-2}. When the car is at A, its speed is u m s^{-1}. The distance AB is 10 m and the car takes 2 s to travel from A to B. The car takes 7 s to travel from A to C and its speed at C is 17 m s^{-1}.

(a) Find the value of u and the value of a. [7]

(b) Draw a velocity–time graph for the motion of the car between A and C. [2]

(c) Calculate the distance AC. [2]

(WJEC M1 June 2011 Q3)

Answers

2 (a)

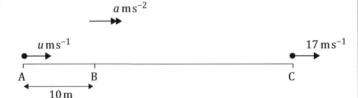

For A to B, $s = 10$, $t = 2$.

Using $s = ut + \frac{1}{2}at^2$

$10 = 2u + \frac{1}{2}at^2$

$10 = 2u + \left(\frac{1}{2} \times a \times 2^2\right)$

$10 = 2u + 2a$ (1)

For A to C, $v = 17$, $t = 7$.

$v = u + at$

$17 = u + 7a$ (2)

Solving equations (1) and (2) simultaneously, we obtain $u = 3$ m s^{-1} and $a = 2$ m s^{-2}.

> Lay out all the information given in the question in a clearly labelled diagram. Once drawn, study the diagram carefully to see what is known and what isn't.

(b) velocity (m s^{-1})

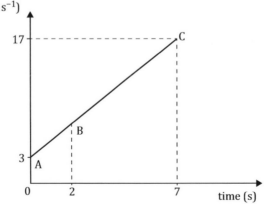

> You can put the value of u which you have just calculated, on the graph.

> A, B and C have been used to denote the various points of the journey but strictly they are points on the road.

(c) The distance AC is the area under the velocity–time graph between A and C.

Area $= \frac{1}{2}(3 + 17) \times 7 = 70$

Distance AC $= 70$ m

> The formula for the area of a trapezium is used here.

Summary: Rectilinear motion

Velocity–time graphs for motion under uniform acceleration

The gradient represents acceleration.

The area under the graph represents the distance/displacement.

A horizontal line represents constant velocity.

Motion under uniform acceleration

$$v = u + at$$
$$s = ut + \tfrac{1}{2}at^2$$
$$v^2 = u^2 + 2as$$
$$s = \tfrac{1}{2}(u + v)t$$

Note that all the equations of motion are **NOT** included in the formula booklet.

s = displacement/distance

u = initial velocity

v = final velocity

a = acceleration

t = time

Vertical motion under gravity

The acceleration due to gravity of 9.8 m s^{-2} acts vertically down.

Remember to decide on which direction to take as positive and then use the equations of motion to find unknown values.

Sketching and interpretation of velocity–time graphs

Use the equations of motion to find unknown quantities if needed.

Remember you are creating a sketch so you do not need a scale along each axis. You only need to include the important values.

Remember to label both sets of axes with the title of the axis and unit.

Many of these graphs are trapezium shaped and the distance/displacement will be the area of a trapezium which can be worked out using the formula:

Area of trapezium = $\tfrac{1}{2}$(sum of the two parallel sides) × perpendicular distance between them.

Topic 2	Dynamics of a particle

This topic covers the following:

- Newton's laws of motion

Newton's laws of motion

Force is a vector quantity as it has both magnitude and direction.

Unbalanced forces produce an acceleration. The unit of force is the Newton (N) and 1 N is the force which causes a 1 kg mass to be accelerated at 1 m s^{-2}.

Newton's first law states that a particle will remain at rest or will continue to move with constant speed in a straight line unless acted upon by some external force. This means that if a particle is acted upon by unbalanced forces then its velocity will change.

Newton's second law states that a resultant force produces an acceleration, according to the formula Force = mass × acceleration or $F = ma$.

Newton's third law states that every action has an equal and opposite reaction. This means that if body A exerts a force on body B, then body B will exert an equal and opposite force on body A.

Using the formula $F = ma$ (Newton's second law) to solve problems

According to Newton's second law of motion, an unbalanced force will produce an acceleration. Take the following situation where we will assume that all the forces act only in the horizontal direction.

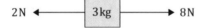

2 N ← 3 kg → 8 N

> Always try to work out the direction of the acceleration and mark this on your diagram.

In order to find the resultant force we resolve the forces in a certain direction. Normally you resolve the forces in the direction of the acceleration. As the resultant force (because the larger of the two forces is to the right) will be to the right, the acceleration will be to the right so we would take the right as the positive direction.

There is a resultant force of 8 − 2 = 6 N to the right and this force will produce an acceleration to the right according to the equation, $F = ma$.

Putting values for the mass and resultant force into this equation gives 6 = 3a, giving $a = 2 \text{ m s}^{-2}$.

Example

❶ For each of the following situations, find the resultant force acting on the block and the acceleration.

(a)

8 N ← 2 kg → 10 N

(b)

6 N ← 2 kg → 2 N

(c)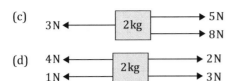
3 N ← [2 kg] → 5 N
→ 8 N

(d) 4 N ← [2 kg] → 2 N
1 N ← → 3 N

Answer

① (a) Resultant force = 10 − 8 = 2 N to the right.

Using $F = ma$,

$$2 = 2a$$

Hence acceleration $a = 1$ m s^{-2} to the right.

(b) Resultant force = 6 − 2 = 4 N to the left.

Using $F = ma$,

$$4 = 2a$$

Hence acceleration $a = 2$ m s^{-2} to the left.

(c) Resultant force = 5 + 8 − 3 = 10 N to the right.

Using $F = ma$,

$$10 = 2a$$

Hence acceleration $a = 5$ m s^{-2} to the right.

(d) Resultant force = (2 + 3) − (4 + 1) = 0 N

Using $F = ma$,

$$0 = 2a$$

Hence acceleration $a = 0$ m s^{-2}.

Types of force

In this topic you will be looking at the effects of certain types of force on a particle. These forces include the following:

- Weight
- Friction
- Normal reaction
- Tension
- Thrust.

Weight is the attractive force between the Earth and the particle. It always acts in a downward direction towards the Earth's centre. Weight can be calculated by multiplying the mass of the particle in kg by the acceleration due to gravity, g, which has the value 9.8 m s^{-2}. Hence

$$\text{Weight} = mg$$

Friction is the force which opposes movement if the surface on which the particle is placed is rough. If you are told that a surface is smooth, then the friction will be zero.

Normal reaction is the force a surface exerts on a particle perpendicular to the surface when there is contact between the two. For example, a particle on a level surface will exert a force (i.e. its weight) vertically down on the surface. According to Newton's third law, the surface will exert an equal but opposite force on the particle for the system to remain in equilibrium. This equal but opposite force is called the normal reaction.

Tension is a resisting force in a string which opposes any tendency for the string to extend. For example, if a particle is hung from a string, the weight of the particle acts down and the tension acts upward to maintain equilibrium.

Thrust is a resisting force provided by a spring. It always acts in a direction to oppose the force that is either compressing or extending the spring.

Example

❶ A block of mass 5 kg rests on a smooth horizontal surface. The block is then subjected to a force of 10 N acting horizontally to the right.

5 kg

(a) Draw a diagram showing all the forces acting on the block.

(b) Find the size of the normal reaction.

(c) Find the acceleration of the block.

Answer

① (a)

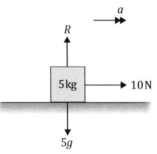

> Always try to work out the direction of the acceleration and mark this on your diagram.

(b) As there is no vertical motion, the vertical forces must be equal.

Hence $R = 5g = 49$ N.

> This is called resolving the forces vertically. As the vertical forces are in equilibrium we can equate the upward force with the downward force.

(c) Resultant force = 10 N to the right.

Using $F = ma$

$$10 = 5a$$

Hence acceleration $a = 2$ m s^{-2} to the right.

> Always remember that acceleration and forces are vector quantities. You should always give their directions unless the question only asks for their magnitude.

Lifts accelerating, decelerating and travelling with constant velocity

This section deals with objects on the floor of lifts when the lift has an acceleration in either direction or when the lift is travelling at constant speed or at rest.

Newton's second law of motion can be applied to each of these situations where all the blocks inside the lift have a mass of m kg. In these situations, the reaction of the lift floor on the body is R upwards.

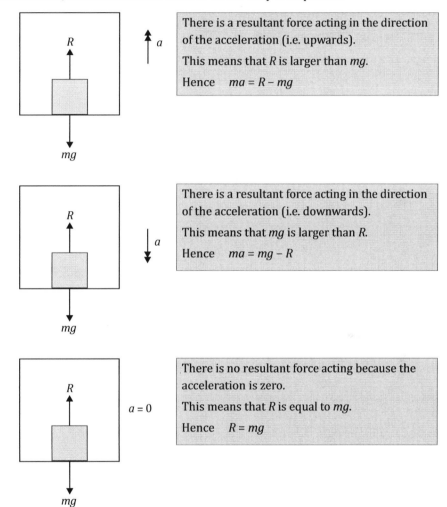

There is a resultant force acting in the direction of the acceleration (i.e. upwards).

This means that R is larger than mg.

Hence $ma = R - mg$

There is a resultant force acting in the direction of the acceleration (i.e. downwards).

This means that mg is larger than R.

Hence $ma = mg - R$

There is no resultant force acting because the acceleration is zero.

This means that R is equal to mg.

Hence $R = mg$

Important note

In the above diagrams the actual direction of movement of the lift has not been included. It is only the direction of the acceleration that is important. For example, the first diagram could apply to either a lift moving upwards with an acceleration a or it could apply to a lift moving downwards which is decelerating with a deceleration a.

Examples

❶   A box, of mass 30 kg, rests on the floor of a lift. Find the reaction of the floor of the lift on the crate when:

(a)   the lift is moving up with acceleration 0.3 m s^{-2},

(b)   the lift is moving down with acceleration 0.2 m s^{-2},

(c)   the lift is moving up with constant speed.

Answer

①   (a)

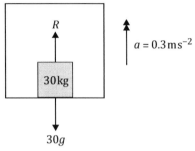

Applying Newton's second law to the box, we have

$$ma = R - mg$$

$$30 \times 0.3 = R - (30 \times 9.8)$$

giving $R = 303$ N

(b)

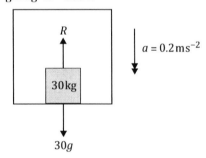

Applying Newton's second law to the box, we have

$$ma = mg - R$$

$$30 \times 0.2 = (30 \times 9.8) - R$$

giving $R = 288$ N

(c)

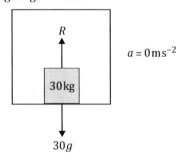

The lift is travelling at constant speed, so the acceleration is zero. The weight and reaction balance so there is no resultant force.

Applying Newton's second law to the box, we have

$$R = mg = 30 \times 9.8 = 294 \text{ N}$$

2 A person, of mass 60 kg, is standing in a lift, which is of mass 540 kg. When the lift is accelerating upwards at a constant rate of a m s^{-2}, the tension in the lift cable is 6600 N.

(a) Calculate the value of a.   [3]

(b) Find the reaction between the person and the floor of the lift.   [3]

(WJEC M1 June 2011 Q2)

Answer

② (a)

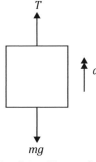

Applying Newton's second law to the lift, we have

$$ma = T - mg$$

Hence $600a = 6600 - (600 \times 9.8)$

giving $a = 1.2$ m s^{-2}

> The mass in this equation is the mass of the lift and the person added together.

(b)

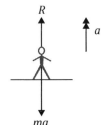

> The only forces acting directly on the person are the weight downwards and the reaction of the lift floor on the person.

Applying Newton's second law to the person, we have

$$ma = R - mg$$

$$60 \times 1.2 = R - (60 \times 9.8)$$

giving $R = 660$ N

3 A lift is moving upwards. It accelerates from rest with uniform acceleration 0.4 m s^{-2} until it reaches a speed of 2 m s^{-1}. It then travels at this constant speed of 2 m s^{-1} for 17 s before decelerating uniformly to rest in 8 s.

(a) Calculate the time taken for the lift to reach the speed of 2 m s^{-1}.   [3]

(b) Sketch a velocity–time graph for the lift's journey.   [3]

(c) Find the distance travelled by the lift during the journey.   [3]

(d) A man, of mass 70 kg, is standing in the lift during its journey.

Calculate the greatest value of the reaction exerted by the floor of the lift on the man during the journey.   [4]

(WJEC M1 Jan 2012 Q1)

Answer

③ (a) Using $v = u + at$ with $v = 2$ m s^{-1}, $u = 0$ m s^{-1}, $a = 0.4$ m s^{-2} we obtain $2 = 0 + (0.4 \times t)$, giving $t = 5$ s.

(b) $v(\text{ms}^{-1})$

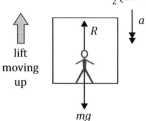

You could, alternatively, split the shape up and find the area of the two triangles and the rectangle and then add them together.

(c) Distance travelled = area under the velocity–time graph.

Area of a trapezium $= \frac{1}{2}$ (sum of the two parallel sides)×distance between the parallel sides

$$= \frac{1}{2}(30 + 17) \times 2 = 47 \text{ m}$$

(d)

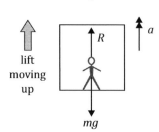

When the lift decelerates when travelling up, applying Newton's second law, we have $ma = mg - R$.

Hence $R = mg - ma = (70 \times 9.8) - (70 \times 0.25) = 668.5$ N

When the lift accelerates when travelling up, applying Newton's second law, we have $ma = R - mg$.

Note that deceleration $= \frac{2}{8} = 0.25$ m s^{-2}

Hence $R = ma + mg = (70 \times 0.4) + (70 \times 9.8) = 714$ N

When the lift is moving at constant speed, $R = 70g = 686$ N

Therefore, the greatest value of the reaction is 714 N.

Motion on an inclined plane

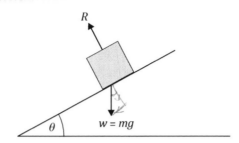

The diagram shows a block of mass m kg, resting on a smooth inclined plane. The plane is inclined at an angle of θ degrees to the horizontal. As there are no frictional forces acting, the only two forces acting are the normal reaction due to the surface, which acts at right angles to the inclined plane and the weight of the block which acts vertically down.

The weight of the block can be converted into two components directed at right angles to each other.

The component of the weight parallel to the slope = $mg \sin \theta$

The component of the weight at right angles to the slope = $mg \cos \theta$

It is important to remember both these components when dealing with objects on inclined planes.

The component of the weight acting down the slope is not balanced by any forces acting up the slope, so it is a resultant force and will therefore cause the block to accelerate down the slope.

We can equate the forces at right angles to the slope because the forces in this direction are in equilibrium.

Resolving at right angles to the slope, we obtain

$$R = mg \cos \theta$$

Applying Newton's second law parallel to the slope, we obtain

$$ma = mg \sin \theta$$

So, $a = g \sin \theta$ (this acceleration will be directed down the slope)

Example

❶   A block of mass 6 kg is placed on a smooth slope inclined at an angle of 30° to the horizontal.

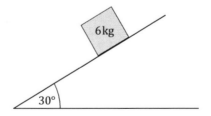

(a)   Copy the diagram and mark on it the weight w and the normal reaction R.

(b)   (i)   Find the magnitude of the component of the weight parallel to the slope.

(ii)   Find the magnitude of the component of the weight at right angles to the slope.

(c)   Find the magnitude of the normal reaction.

(d)   Find the acceleration of the block down the slope.

Answer

① (a)

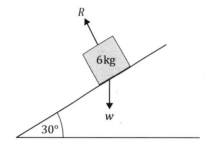

(b) (i) Component of the weight parallel to the slope $= 6g \sin 30°$

$$= 6 \times 9.8 \times 0.5$$

$$= 29.4\,\text{N}$$

(ii) Component of the weight at right angles to the slope $= 6g \cos 30°$

$$= 6 \times 9.8 \times 0.8660$$

$$= 50.9\,\text{N}$$

(c) $R = 50.9\,\text{N}$

(d) Applying Newton's second law parallel to the slope, we obtain

$$ma = 29.4$$

Hence $a = \dfrac{29.4}{6} = 4.9\,\text{m s}^{-2}$

The motion of particles connected by strings passing over fixed pulleys or pegs

When particles are connected by a string passing over a smooth pulley or peg, there is a constant tension in the string provided that the string is light. The forces acting on the particles due to the string are the tensions which act towards the pulley or the peg. The tensions acting on the pulley act in the opposite direction.
Each particle can be treated separately and Newton's second law can be used to form an equation of motion connecting the acceleration to the forces acting.

When both particles are hanging freely

In the arrangement shown, two masses of 6 kg and 8 kg are connected by a light inextensible string passing over a smooth pulley. The masses are originally at rest and then released.

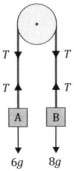

Accelerations are of equal magnitude because the string is inextensible.

When the system shown above is released, the heavier particle (B in this case) will accelerate downwards and the other particle (A in this case) will accelerate upwards. Both accelerations will be equal in magnitude but opposite in direction.

Newton's second law of motion can be applied to each mass separately.

Applying Newton's second law of motion to mass A, we obtain

$$ma = T - 6g$$

so $6a = T - 6g$ (1)

Applying Newton's second law of motion to mass B, we obtain

$$ma = 8g - T$$

so $8a = 8g - T$ (2)

You now have two equations, with two unknowns, which can be solved simultaneously to determine a and T.

Adding equations (1) and (2) we have

$$14a = 2g$$
$$14a = 2 \times 9.8$$

Hence $a = 1.4\,\text{m s}^{-2}$

> Remember to check the two values satisfy equation (2) by substituting them in and checking that the left-hand side of the equation equals the right-hand side.

Substituting this value for a into equation (1) we have

$$6 \times 1.4 = T - (6 \times 9.8)$$

Hence $T = 67.2\,\text{N}$

When one particle is freely hanging and the other particle is on a smooth horizontal plane

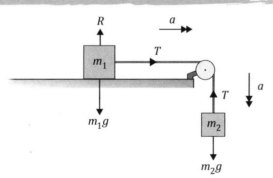

> Again note that the accelerations are equal because the string is inextensible. The tension is constant because the string is assumed to be light.

As there is no vertical motion for mass m_1 the vertical forces are in equilibrium.

Resolving vertically gives $R = m_1 g$

Applying Newton's second law of motion to mass m_1 we obtain

$$m_1 a = T \qquad\qquad\qquad (1)$$

Applying Newton's second law of motion to mass m_2 we obtain

$$m_2 a = m_2 g - T \qquad\qquad\qquad (2)$$

Then a and T are again found by solving the simultaneous equations (1) and (2).

When one particle is freely hanging and the other particle is on a smooth inclined plane

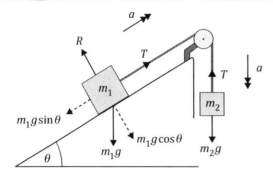

In this arrangement, the block on the inclined plane is accelerating up the slope. You can also get the situation where the mass would accelerate down the slope. For practice you should write the set of equations for this new situation.

As there is no motion of mass m_1 perpendicular to the plane, the forces acting perpendicular to the plane must be in equilibrium.

Resolving the forces on m_1 perpendicular to the plane, we obtain

$$R = m_1 g \cos \theta$$

Applying Newton's second law of motion to mass m_1 we obtain

$$m_1 a = T - m_1 g \sin \theta$$

Applying Newton's second law of motion to mass m_2 we obtain

$$m_2 a = m_2 g - T$$

Example

❶ The diagram shows a particle A, on a **smooth** inclined plane, joined by a light inextensible string passing over a smooth pulley to a particle B, which hangs freely. The plane is inclined at an angle α to the horizontal, where $\sin \alpha = \frac{5}{13}$. The masses of A and B are 13 kg and 15 kg respectively. The string is in the same vertical plane as a line of greatest slope of the plane.

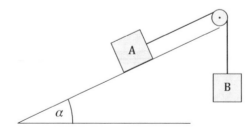

Initially, the particles are held at rest with the string taut. The system is released. Calculate the magnitude of the acceleration of the particle A and the tension in the string. [7]

(WJEC M1 June 2011 Q5)

Answer

①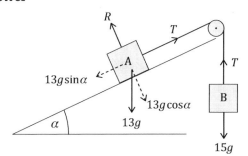

As the surface of the slope is smooth there is no frictional force acting. All the other forces are marked on the diagram. Notice that the weight of A (i.e. $13g$) can be resolved into two components; one $13g \sin \alpha$ parallel to the plane and the other $13g \cos \alpha$ at right angles to the plane.

We will assume that when released particle A will accelerate up the slope as particle B moves vertically down.

Applying Newton's second law to particle A for motion up the plane, we have

$$ma = T - 13g \sin \alpha$$
$$13a = T - (13 \times 9.8 \times \tfrac{5}{13})$$
$$13a = T - 49 \qquad (1)$$

Notice there are two unknowns in this equation (i.e. a and T). Another equation is needed also containing the two unknowns so they can be found using simultaneous equations.

Applying Newton's second law to particle B, we have

$$ma = 15g - T$$
$$15a = (15 \times 9.8) - T$$
$$15a = 147 - T \qquad (2)$$

Solving equations (1) and (2) simultaneously gives $a = 3.5 \text{ m s}^{-2}$ and $T = 94.5$ N.

Examination style questions

❶ A lift has a mass of 450 kg. A man with a mass of 50 kg stands in the lift and the tension in the lift cable is 4000 N when the lift is descending with an acceleration of a m s^{-2}.

(a) Find the value of a. [3]

(b) Find the reaction between the floor of the lift and the man. [4]

Answer

① (a)

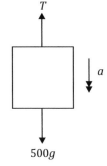

Note that here the mass m refers to the total mass of the lift and the man.

Applying Newton's second law of motion to the lift including the man, we obtain

$$ma = 500g - T$$
$$500a = (500 \times 9.8) - 4000$$
$$a = 1.8 \text{ m s}^{-2}$$

(b)

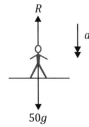

The only forces acting directly on the man are his weight and the reaction of the lift floor upon him.

Applying Newton's second law of motion to the man in the lift, we obtain

$$ma = 50g - R$$
$$50 \times 1.8 = (50 \times 9.8) - R$$
$$R = 400 \text{ N}$$

m is now the mass of the man only.

❷ Two identical buckets A and B are tied to a light inextensible rope which is passed over a smooth pulley as shown in diagram.

Both buckets have a mass of 0.4 kg.

(a) State the magnitude of the tension in the rope. [2]

(b) Bucket A is held at rest while sand of mass 4.6 kg is added to bucket B. The system is then released from rest and bucket B travels downward with the sand inside.

  (i) Using Newton's second law of motion, form two equations, one for each bucket. [4]

  (ii) Solving the equations formed in part (i), find the acceleration of the system and the tension in the rope. [4]

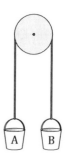

Answer

② (a)

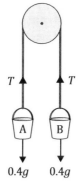

Resolving vertically for bucket A, we obtain $T = 0.4g = 0.4 \times 9.8 = 3.92\,\text{N}$

(b)

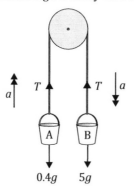

In this case, the combined mass of bucket B and sand is 5 kg. Note that the tensions are different from those in part (a).

(i) Applying Newton's second law of motion to A, we obtain

Note the different values of m for A and B.

$$ma = T - 0.4g$$
$$0.4a = T - 0.4g \quad (1)$$

Applying Newton's second law of motion to B, we obtain

$$ma = 5g - T$$
$$5a = 5g - T \quad (2)$$

(ii) Solving equations (1) and (2) simultaneously, we obtain

$$a = 8.35\,\text{m s}^{-2} \text{ and } T = 7.26\,\text{N}$$

Test yourself

❶ A particle of mass 3 kg is attached to the end of a light inextensible string and allowed to hang vertically. The string and particle are accelerated vertically downwards with an acceleration of $2\,\text{m}\,\text{s}^{-2}$.

Calculate the tension in the string.

❷ Two particles of mass 1.5 kg and 2 kg are connected by a light inextensible string that passes over a smooth peg. The particles are released from rest as shown in the diagram.

(a) By using Newton's second law of motion, form an equation of motion for each particle and hence show that the tension in the string is 16.8 N.

(b) Find the acceleration of the system.

(c) If the particles are initially at the same level, determine the speed of the heavier particle when the distance between the two particles is 1 m.

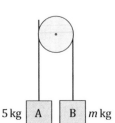

1.5 kg   2 kg

❸ A light inextensible string connects particles P of mass 5 kg and Q of mass 8 kg. Particle P lies on a smooth inclined plane which is inclined at an angle of 30° to the horizontal. The string passes over a smooth pulley and both particles are released from rest. The system is shown below.

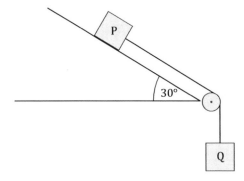

(a) Find the acceleration of the system.

(b) Find the tension in the string.

❹ Particles A and B are connected by a light inextensible string which moves over a smooth pulley and this system is shown in the following diagram.

The mass of particle A is 5 kg and the mass of particle B is m kg where $m > 5$.

The particles are released from rest with the strings taut and vertical.

When the particles are released, the magnitude of the common acceleration of the particles is $2\,\text{m}\,\text{s}^{-2}$.

5 kg A   B m kg

(a) Find the value of the tension in the string.

(b) Find the value of m.

1   A lift is pulled upwards by means of a vertical cable. Initially, the lift is at rest. It then accelerates until it reaches a maximum speed. The lift moves at this maximum speed before decelerating uniformly at 3 m s^{-2} to rest. The total mass of the lift and its contents is 360 kg.

(a) Calculate the tension in the lift cable:

    (i)   when the lift is decelerating

    (ii) when the lift is moving at its maximum speed.   [4]

(b) A crate on the floor of the lift has a mass of 25 kg. When the lift is accelerating the reaction between the crate and the floor of the lift is 280 N.

    Find the magnitude of the acceleration of the lift.   [3]

(WJEC M1 Jan 2010 Q2)

Answer

1   (a) (i)

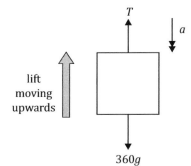

Applying Newton's second law in the vertical direction, we have

$$360a = 360g - T$$

$$360 \times 3 = (360 \times 9.8) - T$$

Giving $T = 2448$ N

(ii) When the lift is moving at constant speed there is no acceleration and therefore no resultant force.

Hence the tension is in equilibrium with the weight.

$$T = mg = 360 \times 9.8 = 3528 \text{ N}$$

(b)

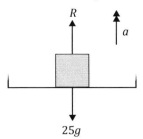

Applying Newton's second law in the vertical direction for the crate, we have

$$25a = R - 25g$$

$$25a = 280 - 25 \times 9.8$$

Hence $a = 1.4 \text{ m s}^{-2}$

2   The diagram shows two objects A and B, of mass 5 kg and 9 kg respectively, connected by a light inextensible string passing over a smooth peg. Initially, the objects are held at rest. The system is then released.

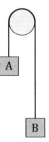

(a) Find the magnitude of the acceleration of A and the tension in the string.   [7]

(b) What assumption did the word 'light', underlined in the first sentence, enable you to make in your solution?   [1]

(WJEC M1 Jan 2012 Q5)

Answer

2   (a)

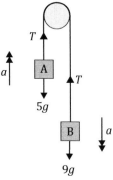

Applying Newton's second law of motion to A, we have

$$ma = T - 5g$$
$$5a = T - 5g \qquad (1)$$

Applying Newton's second law of motion to B, we have

$$ma = 9g - T$$
$$9a = 9g - T \qquad (2)$$

Adding equations (1) and (2), we obtain

$$14a = 4g$$
$$14a = 4 \times 9.8$$

Hence $a = 2.8 \, \text{m s}^{-2}$

From (1), $T = 5a + 5g = 63 \, \text{N}$

(b) The assumption of a light string enables us to regard the tension T as being constant throughout the string.

Summary: Dynamics of a particle

Newton's second law of motion

Unbalanced forces produce an acceleration according to the equation

Force = mass × acceleration   or for short $F = ma$

Lifts accelerating, decelerating and travelling with constant velocity

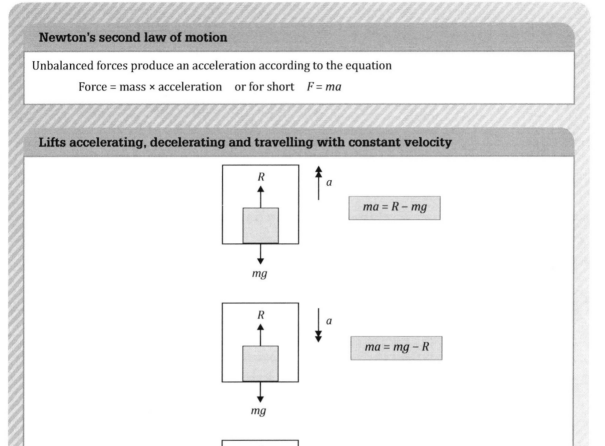

$$ma = R - mg$$

$$ma = mg - R$$

$$R = mg$$

Motion on an inclined plane

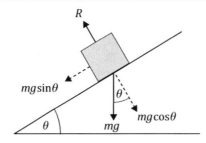

The component of the weight parallel to the slope = $mg \sin \theta$

The component of the weight at right angles to the slope = $mg \cos \theta$

The motion of particles connected by strings passing over fixed pulleys or pegs

Pulleys or pegs are smooth so no frictional forces act.

Strings are light and inextensible so the tension remains constant.

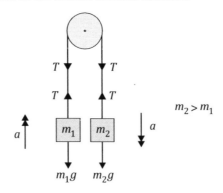

Acceleration of each mass is the same as the string is taut.

Newton's second law can be applied to each mass separately.

For m_1, $m_1 a = T - m_1 g$ and, for m_2, $m_2 a = m_2 g - T$

Topic 3 | Friction

This topic covers the following:

- Laws of friction
- Limiting friction and the coefficient of friction

Friction

Friction is a force which opposes motion and occurs when two surfaces are in contact.

If the particle shown on the right is stationary and there is no horizontal force acting, then the frictional force will be zero. The only forces acting will be the weight mg acting downwards, which will be in equilibrium with the normal reaction R acting upwards.

If a particle is subjected to a horizontal force T but does not move, then the frictional force F must be equal to the horizontal force. The force of friction is equal and opposite to the horizontal force.

If a particle is subjected to a horizontal force T that is larger than the frictional force F, then there will be a resultant force (i.e. $T - F$) which will cause the particle to accelerate. In the case shown in the diagram, the particle will move to the right with an acceleration a m s^{-2}.

Newton's second law of motion can be applied and we obtain

$$ma = T - F$$

As $T > F$, there will be resultant force to the right, which will produce an acceleration also to the right. We use the direction of the acceleration as the positive direction.

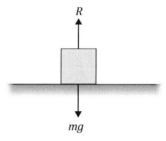

Resolving vertically, we obtain
$R = mg$

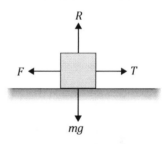

Resolving vertically, we obtain
$R = mg$.

Resolving horizontally, we obtain
$F = T$ for equilibrium.

Laws of friction

There are a number of laws which can be applied to situations where friction occurs and these are summarised here:

- For two bodies in contact, the force of friction opposes the relative motion of the bodies.
- If bodies are in equilibrium, the force of friction is just sufficient to prevent motion and can be found by resolving the forces parallel to the surface.
- The size of the frictional force which can be exerted between two bodies is limited. If the force acting on a body is great enough, then motion will occur. Limiting friction is the frictional force exerted when equilibrium is on the point of being broken.

Example

❶ A particle of mass 4 kg is pulled along a **rough** horizontal surface by a 20 N force. If the frictional force is 8 N, and the particle is initially at rest, calculate:

(a) the acceleration of the particle, and

(b) the distance covered by the particle in the first 5 seconds.

Answer

① (a)

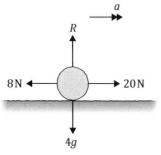

Always check the question to see if a surface is rough or smooth. If a surface is smooth, then no frictional forces will act (i.e. $F = 0$).

Looking at the sizes of the horizontal forces you can see that the force to the right is greater than the force to the left. The resultant force and hence the acceleration will be to the right. We usually take the direction of the acceleration as the positive direction when considering forces.

Applying Newton's second law, we obtain

$$ma = 20 - 8$$

$$4a = 12$$

$$a = 3 \text{ m s}^{-2}$$

The resultant force is 20 – 8 to the right and this is used to accelerate the mass according to the equation, $F = ma$.

(b) $u = 0, a = 3, t = 5, s = ?$

Using $s = ut + \frac{1}{2}at^2$ we have

$$s = (0 \times 5) + \left(\frac{1}{2} \times 3 \times 5^2\right) = 37.5 \text{ m}$$

The equations of motion are used here. Remember that these will not be given so you need to memorise them.

Limiting friction and the coefficient of friction

When a particle is on a rough horizontal surface and an increasing horizontal force is applied, there comes a point when the particle will start to move. This is because the frictional force can increase to oppose the force trying to make it move only up to a certain amount. This amount is called the maximum or limiting friction.

This maximum or limiting value for the frictional force depends on the following two things:

- The size of the normal reaction between the two surfaces in contact.

- The roughness of the two surfaces in contact.

The roughness of the surfaces in contact is measured using a quantity called the coefficient of friction which is given the symbol, μ.

The maximum or limiting frictional force between two surfaces can be found using the following equation:

Limiting friction, $F = \mu R$

This equation can also be expressed in the following way

$$F_{MAX} = \mu R,$$

where μ is the coefficient of friction and R is the normal reaction between the surfaces.

If you are dealing with an object on the point of moving or actually moving, then the object will experience the maximum frictional force.

When a force P acts on a block of mass m on a rough horizontal surface the maximum (or limiting) value that F can take is given by $F_{MAX} = \mu R$.

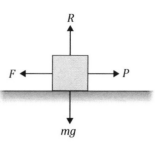

There are three situations that can occur as the force P varies and they are:

- When $P < F_{MAX}$, the frictional force F will be equal to P and as these forces balance, the block will be in equilibrium and remain at rest.

- When $P = F_{MAX}$, the frictional force has reached its maximum value. The block experiences limiting friction and is just on the point of moving.

- When $P > F_{MAX}$ then there will be a resultant force which will start to accelerate the block. Throughout the motion, the frictional force will be at its maximum value.

Examples

❶ An object, of mass 5 kg, lies on a **rough** horizontal surface. The coefficient of friction between the object and the surface is 0.6. A horizontal force of magnitude T N is applied to the object.

(a) Given that $T = 40$, calculate the magnitude of the frictional force and the acceleration of the object. *[5]*

(b) Given that $T = 20$, describes what happens, giving a reason for your answer. *[2]*

(WJEC M1 Jan 2010 Q6)

Answer

① (a)

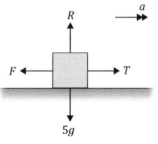

Draw a diagram and mark on it all the forces acting on the object. Also mark the direction of the acceleration, which will be in the direction of the resultant force. Take this direction as the positive direction.

Resolving forces in the vertical direction, we obtain

$$R = 5g$$
$$R = 5 \times 9.8 = 49 \text{ N}$$

The forces are balanced in the vertical direction, so the normal reaction, R, is equal and opposite to the weight $5g$.

Limiting friction, $F = \mu R = 0.6 \times 49 = 29.4 \text{ N}$

Applying Newton's second law in the horizontal direction, we have

$$ma = T - F$$
$$5a = 40 - 29.4$$

giving $\qquad a = 2.12 \text{ m s}^{-2}$

(b) The particle will remain at rest.

T is 20 N which is less than the limiting friction of 29.4 N. The frictional force will therefore be equal to 20 N and there will be no resultant force, no acceleration and no motion.

❷ A mass of 10 kg is at rest on a **rough** horizontal surface. It is attached by a light string which passes over a smooth pulley to a mass of 5 kg which hangs vertically. The arrangement is shown in the following diagram.

The coefficient of friction between the block and the surface is 0.2 and the system is released from rest and the block accelerates with an acceleration, a.

(a) Find the magnitude of the friction force acting on the 10 kg block.

(b) Find the acceleration of the system, a.

(c) Find the tension in the string.

Answer

② (a)

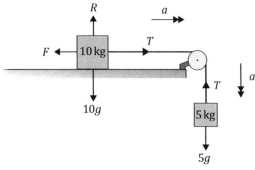

> Draw a diagram showing all the forces acting on each block and also mark the direction of the acceleration of each block.

Resolving vertically for the 10 kg mass, we obtain

$$R = 10g = 98 \text{ N}$$

Limiting friction $\quad F = \mu R = 0.2 \times 98 = 19.6 \text{ N}$

> Remember that friction can take any value up to a certain maximum value which can be referred to either as limiting friction or F_{MAX}. As the block is moving, it will experience the maximum friction.

(b) Resolving horizontally and applying Newton's second law to the 10 kg mass, we obtain

$$ma = T - F$$
$$10a = T - 19.6 \qquad (1)$$

Resolving vertically and applying Newton's second law to the 5 kg mass, we obtain

$$5a = 5g - T$$

so $\quad 5a = 49 - T \qquad (2)$

Adding equations (1) and (2) we obtain

$$15a = 29.4$$
$$a = 1.96 \text{ m s}^{-2}$$

⚔ Grade boost

Do not make the mistake of including either the weight or the normal reaction in this equation. Both of these act only in the vertical direction and the equations of motion refer only to horizontal motion.

(c) Substituting the value of a into equation (1) we obtain

$$19.6 = T - 19.6$$
$$T = 39.2 \text{ N}$$

⚔ Grade boost

Remember to check the values by substituting them into equation (2) and check that the left-hand side of the equation equals the right-hand side.

❸ The diagram shows an object, of mass 8 kg, on a **rough** plane
inclined at an angle of 15° to the horizontal.

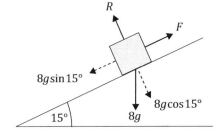

(a) Given that the object is at rest, calculate the least possible value
of the coefficient of friction. Give your answer correct to two
decimal places. *[6]*

(b) Given that the coefficient of friction is 0.1, find the acceleration of the object down the plane. *[4]*

(WJEC M1 June 2011 Q6)

Answer

③ (a)

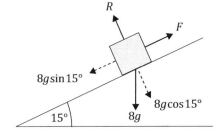

> Remember that when you deal with objects on slopes
> you need to use the components of the weight at right
> angles to the slope and parallel to the slope.

> The component of the weight parallel to the slope will
> need a balancing force (i.e. friction in this case) if the
> object is to remain at rest.

Component of the weight parallel to the plane = $8g \sin 15°$

Component of the weight at right angles to the plane = $8g \cos 15°$

(Note both these forces are marked on the diagram and we can disregard the weight as it has been
replaced by its two components.)

The least value of the frictional force is when it just balances the component of the weight acting
down the slope.

Hence, resolving forces parallel to the slope, we obtain

$$F = 8g \sin 15° = 8 \times 9.8 \sin 15° = 20.29 \text{ N}$$

Resolving perpendicular to the slope, we obtain

$$R = 8g \cos 15° = 75.73 \text{ N}$$

Limiting friction $F = \mu R$

Hence $\quad \mu = \dfrac{F}{R} = \dfrac{20.29}{75.73} = 0.27$ (correct to two decimal places)

⊼ Grade boost

You must say that this is
limiting friction or F_{MAX}.

(b) Limiting friction, $F = \mu R = 0.1 \times 75.73 = 7.57$ N

Applying Newton's second law, we obtain

$$ma = mg \sin 15° - F$$
$$8a = 8 \times 9.8 \sin 15° - 7.57$$

Hence $\quad a = 1.59 \text{ m s}^{-2}$

> This is the maximum friction
> that can occur and this value
> will be the friction acting on
> the block when it is moving.

Examination style questions

1 Two particles P and Q are connected by a light string. Particle P has a mass of 5 kg and lies on a **rough** horizontal table. The string passes over a smooth pulley on the edge of the table and particle Q of mass 8 kg hangs vertically at the other end of the string. Particle Q is then released from rest at a height of 1.5 m above the ground and it takes a time of 1 s to hit the ground.

Find the tension in the string, the acceleration of the particles and the frictional force acting on P.   *[6]*

Answer

①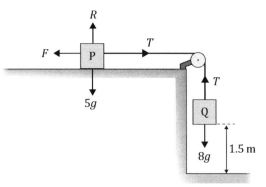

> This question is harder because no diagram is included. You need to draw your own and mark the forces and other information on it.

For particle Q, we have $u = 0$, $s = 1.5$, $t = 1$, $a = ?$

Using $s = ut + \frac{1}{2}at^2$

$1.5 = 0 + \left(\frac{1}{2} \times a \times 1^2\right)$

$a = 3 \text{ m s}^{-2}$

> One of the equations of motion is used here to calculate the acceleration of the system when particle Q is released from rest.

Applying Newton's second law to particle Q, we have

$8a = 8g - T$

$8 \times 3 = (8 \times 9.8) - T$

$T = 54.4 \text{ N}$

Applying Newton's second law to particle P, we have

$ma = T - F$

$5 \times 3 = 54.4 - F$

$F = 39.4 \text{ N}$

2 The diagram shows two blocks, P with a mass of 5 kg and Q with a mass of 3 kg. Both blocks are connected by a light inextensible string passing over a smooth pulley. Block P is situated on a **rough** horizontal table and particle Q hangs vertically below the pulley.

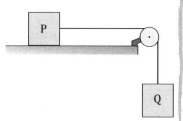

Initially, the system is held at rest with the string just taut. The system is then released.

(a) If the coefficient of friction between P and the table is 0.3, find the magnitude of the acceleration of particle P and the tension in the string.   *[9]*

(b) When released, the particles now remain stationary. Find the least value of the coefficient of friction for this to happen.   *[3]*

Answer

② (a)

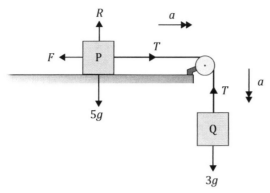

Resolving vertically for block P, we obtain

$$R = 5g$$

Limiting friction $F = \mu R$

$$= 0.3 \times 5g$$

$$= 1.5g$$

Applying Newton's second law to block P, we have

$$ma = T - F$$

$$5a = T - 1.5g \qquad\qquad (1)$$

Applying Newton's second law to block Q, we have

$$3a = 3g - T \qquad\qquad (2)$$

Adding equations (1) and (2), we obtain

$$8a = 1.5g$$

$$a = 1.84 \text{ m s}^{-2}$$

Substituting the value of a into equation (1), we obtain

$$5 \times 1.84 = T - (1.5 \times 9.8)$$

$$T = 23.89 \text{ N}$$

> It is assumed that the tension is greater than the limiting friction so that P moves to the right.

> Don't forget to check these two values (i.e. a and T) by substituting them back into equation (2). The left-hand side of the equation should equal the right-hand side.

(b) When the blocks are stationary, acceleration $a = 0$. This means that for each block, the forces are in equilibrium.

Resolving forces vertically for block P, we obtain

$$R = 5g$$

Resolving forces vertically for block Q, we obtain

$$T = 3g$$

Applying Newton's second law of motion horizontally for block P, we obtain

$$ma = T - F$$

Now $F_{\text{MAX}} = \mu R = 5\mu g$ and $a = 0$, so

$$0 = 3g - 5\mu g$$

Hence, least value of $\mu = 0.6$

> Do not use the value of T as calculated in part (a) as the tension will be different when the particles are not accelerating.

> Here the values of F, a and T are substituted into the equation $ma = T - F$

Test yourself

❶ A horizontal force of 40 N acts on a block of mass 5 kg causing it to move in a straight line along a **rough** horizontal surface. The arrangement is shown in the diagram.

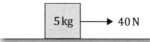

(a) Draw a diagram showing all the forces acting on the block.

(b) Find the magnitude of the normal reaction acting on the block.

(c) If the acceleration of the block is 2 m s⁻², calculate the magnitude of the frictional force acting on the block.

❷ A particle of mass 3 kg lies at rest on a **rough** horizontal surface. The coefficient of friction between the particle and surface is 0.3.

(a) Find the magnitude of the frictional force and the acceleration of the particle, if a horizontal force P of magnitude 8 N is applied to the block.

(b) Find the magnitude of the frictional force and the acceleration of the particle, if a horizontal force P of magnitude 12 N is applied to the block.

❸ A box of mass 6 kg rests on a **rough** plane inclined at an angle of 20° to the horizontal.

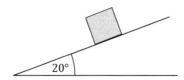

(a) Calculate the least value of the coefficient of friction, if the box is to remain at rest on the slope. Give your answer correct to two significant figures.

(b) If the coefficient of friction is 0.2, calculate the acceleration of the box down the slope.

Q&A 1

1   The diagram shows an object A, of mass 6 kg, lying on a rough horizontal table. The object A is connected by means of a light inextensible string passing over a smooth pulley at the edge of the table to another object B, of mass 4 kg, hanging freely.

The coefficient of friction between object A and the table is 0.4. Initially, the system is held at rest with the string just taut. The system is then released.

(a) Find the magnitude of the acceleration of object A and the tension in the string.   [9]

(b) What assumption did the word 'light' underlined above enable you to make in your solution?   [1]

(WJEC M1 June 2010 Q5)

Answer

1   (a)

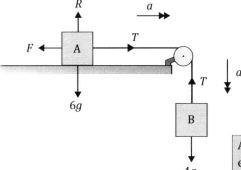

As object A is accelerating, it will experience the maximum frictional force.

Resolving vertically for A, we have

$$R = 6g$$

Limiting friction, $F = \mu R = 0.4 \times 6g = 2.4g$

Applying Newton's second law to particle A, we have

$$ma = T - F$$
$$6a = T - 2.4g \qquad (1)$$

Applying Newton's second law to particle B, we have

$$ma = 4g - T$$
$$4a = 4g - T \qquad (2)$$

Adding equations (1) and (2), we obtain

$$10a = 1.6g$$
$$10a = 1.6 \times 9.8$$

Hence $a = 1.57 \text{ m s}^{-2}$

Substituting this value of a into equation (1), we obtain

Remember to check these solutions of the simultaneous equations by substituting the values back into equation (2) and check that they fit the equation.

$$6 \times 1.57 = T - (2.4 \times 9.8)$$

Hence $T = 32.93 \text{ N}$

(b) The tension is constant in the string.

2   A rough plane is inclined at an angle α to the horizontal where $\sin\alpha = \frac{3}{5}$. A body of mass 80 kg lies on the plane. The coefficient of friction between the body and the plane is μ.

   (a)   Find the normal reaction of the plane on the body.   [2]

   (b)   The body is on the point of slipping down the plane. Find the value of μ.   [4]

   (c)   Calculate the magnitude of the force acting along a line of greatest slope that will move the body up the plane with an acceleration of 0.7 m s^{-2}.   [4]

   (WJEC M1 Jan 2012 Q3)

Answer

2   (a)

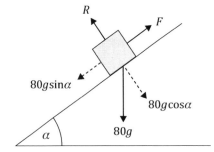

If $\sin\alpha = \frac{3}{5}$, $\cos\alpha = \frac{4}{5}$

Resolving at right angles to the plane, we have

$R = mg\cos\alpha = 80 \times 9.8 \times 0.8 = 627.2$ N

   (b)   As there is no acceleration along the slope the forces parallel to the slope are in equilibrium (i.e. frictional force is equal to the component of the weight down the slope).

Resolving parallel to the slope, we obtain

$$F = 80g\sin\alpha = 80 \times 9.8 \times \frac{3}{5} = 470.4 \text{ N}$$

This is limiting friction.

On the point of slipping, $F = \mu R$

Hence $\mu = \dfrac{F}{R} = \dfrac{470.4}{627.2} = 0.75$

   (c)

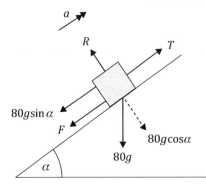

Notice that the forces at right angles to the plane have not altered, so $R = 627.2$ N.

Also, the magnitude of the frictional force will not change but its direction is now down the slope.

Hence $F = 470.4$ N.

Applying Newton's second law parallel to the slope, we have

$$ma = T - 80g\sin\alpha - F$$

$$80 \times 0.7 = T - \left(80 \times 9.8 \times \frac{3}{5}\right) - 470.4$$

giving $T = 996.8$ N

Summary: Friction

Friction opposes motion

It can increase up to a certain maximum value called limiting friction or F_{MAX}.

Limiting friction, $F = \mu R$ which can also be written as $F_{MAX} = \mu R$, where μ is the coefficient of friction and R is the normal reaction between the surfaces.

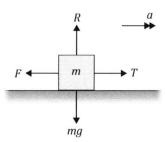

If $T > F$ there will be an unbalanced force and the mass will accelerate.

By Newton's second law $ma = T - F$

Once moving, the mass will experience the maximum frictional force given by

$$F_{MAX} = \mu R$$

The forces are balanced in the vertical direction, so $R = mg$

Topic 4 — Momentum and impulse

This topic covers the following:

- Momentum and impulse
- Conservation of momentum
- Newton's experimental law for the direct impact of two bodies moving in the same straight line
- Newton's experimental law for the impact of a body moving at right angles to a plane

Momentum and impulse

Momentum

Momentum = mass × velocity

The unit of momentum is kg m s^{-1} and as momentum is a vector quantity, it has both size and direction.

Impulse

If a constant force F acts on a body for a time t seconds, then the impulse I of the force is given by the equation:

$I = Ft$ This equation should be remembered as it will not be given.

Since force F is measured in newtons and time t is measured in seconds, the units for impulse, I are N s. There is also another unit that can be used for impulse which is kg m s^{-1}.

Impulse can be expressed in terms of momentum as follows:

Impulse, I = Change in momentum

I = Final momentum − Initial momentum

$I = mv - mu$

where u is the initial velocity, v is the final velocity and m is the mass.

It is sometimes useful to express the above equation in the following way:

$I = m(v - u)$ This equation needs to be remembered.

Example

1 A ball having a mass of 0.4 kg travels in a straight horizontal path and hits a fixed vertical wall with a velocity of 4 m s^{-1}. If the ball rebounds with a speed of 3 m s^{-1}, find the size of the impulse exerted by the wall on the ball.

4 m s^{-1}

3 m s^{-1}

Answer

① Regarding to the right as the positive direction, we obtain

$$I = mv - mu$$

$$I = m(v - u)$$

$$I = 0.4(-3 - 4)$$

$$I = -2.8\,N\,s$$

> Initial velocity, $u = 4\,m\,s^{-1}$ and final velocity, $v = 3\,m\,s^{-1}$. Note that we have taken positive direction as to the right. Hence as the final velocity is reversed it has a negative sign.

> This is the impulse of the wall on the ball. The impulse of the ball on the wall will be equal in magnitude to this but opposite in direction (i.e. positive rather than negative).

Hence the size of the impulse of the wall on the ball = 2.8 N s

Conservation of momentum

The law of conservation of momentum states that the total momentum before a collision is equal to the total momentum after the collision provided that no external forces act.

Before collision

After collision

> The initial velocities, u_A and u_B are written above the particles and the final velocities v_A and v_B are written below the particles.
>
> You have to decide on which direction to take as the positive direction. The positive direction is taken to the right here.

Applying the law of conservation of momentum, we obtain

$$m_A u_A + m_B u_B = m_A v_A + m_B v_B$$

Note that, in the above diagram, velocities to the right are taken as positive.

Newton's experimental law for the direct impact of two bodies moving in the same straight line

Newton's experimental law describes how the velocity of separation of two impacting bodies compares with their velocity of approach. Consider the following spheres with equal radii moving along the same straight line.

u_A = initial velocity of mass A

u_B = initial velocity of mass B

v_A = final velocity of mass A

v_B = final velocity of mass B

The coefficient of restitution (e) is a number which can take any value between and including 0 and 1 (i.e. $0 \leq e \leq 1$).

Coefficient of restitution, e, can be calculated using the velocities outlined above using the following equation:

$$\frac{v_B - v_A}{u_B - u_A} = -e$$

> This equation will need to be remembered.

It is also useful to use the rearranged form of the above equation:

$$v_B - v_A = -e(u_B - u_A)$$

Examples

❶ Two bodies A and B are at rest on a smooth horizontal surface. Body A has mass 2 kg and body B has mass 16 kg. Body A is projected with speed 3 m s^{-1} towards body B and collides directly with it. The coefficient of restitution between bodies A and B is $\frac{1}{2}$.

(a) Find the speeds of A and B after the collision.

(b) Determine the magnitude and direction of the impulse exerted by body B on body A, stating your units.

Answer

① (a)

Regard the right as the positive direction.

Applying conservation of momentum, we obtain

$$(2 \times 3) + (16 \times 0) = 2v_A + 16v_B$$
$$6 = 2v_A + 16v_B$$
$$3 = v_A + 8v_B \qquad (1)$$

> Divide through by 2.

Applying Newton's law of restitution, we obtain

$$\frac{v_B - v_A}{u_B - u_A} = -e$$

$$\frac{v_B - v_A}{0 - 3} = -\frac{1}{2}$$

$$2v_B - 2v_A = 3$$

$$v_B - v_A = \frac{3}{2} \qquad (2)$$

Adding equation (1) and (2) gives

$$9v_B = 4.5$$

Hence $\qquad v_B = 0.5 \text{ m s}^{-1}$

Substituting this value into equation (1), we obtain

$$3 = v_A + (8 \times 0.5)$$

Hence $\qquad v_A = -1 \text{ m s}^{-1}$

> The negative sign tells us that A is now travelling to the left (i.e. the opposite to the direction we defined as being positive).

(b) Impulse, I = change in momentum of A

$$I = m(v - u)$$
$$I = 2(-1 - 3)$$
$$I = -8 \, \text{N s}$$

> The question asks to determine the magnitude and direction of the impulse exerted by body B on body A. This means that we need to find the change in momentum of A.

The impulse exerted by B on A = 8 N s
directed to the left.

❷ Two particles A and B with masses 3 kg and 2 kg respectively are travelling horizontally in the same straight line and in the same direction. Particle A is travelling with speed 20 m s^{-1} and particle B is travelling with speed 10 m s^{-1}.

Particles A and B collide and coalesce (i.e. become a single particle). Find the speed of this particle after the collision.

Answer

② 　　　　　　　　before　　　　　　　　　　　　　after

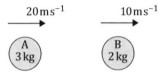

Regard the right as the positive direction.

Applying conservation of momentum, we obtain

$$(3 \times 20) + (2 \times 10) = 5v$$

giving 　　　　　　　　$v = 16 \, \text{m s}^{-1}$

> Note that the mass of the new particle will be the masses of the two colliding particles combined.

Newton's experimental law for the impact of a body moving at right angles to a plane

For an object bouncing off a plane at right angles to its path such as a wall:

$$e = \frac{v}{u}$$

> This equation will need to be remembered.

where

　　e is the coefficient of restitution between the object and the wall,

　　v is the speed of the object after impact,

　　u is the speed of the object before impact.

> Note that this means that u and v cannot have negative values.

Important note: You do not put any signs into this equation, just the numbers.

Examples

1 Sphere A is travelling with a speed of 10 m s^{-1} in a straight horizontal line towards a fixed vertical wall with which it collides. The sphere rebounds off the wall with a speed of 8 m s^{-1}. Find the coefficient of restitution between the sphere and the wall.

Answer

① Coefficient of restitution, $e = \dfrac{v}{u}$

$\qquad\qquad\qquad = \dfrac{8}{10} = 0.8$

> Note that the coefficient of restitution has no units. Also as a check, it has to have a value of between and including 0 and 1. It therefore can only have non-negative values.

2 A sphere A of mass 2 kg travelling at a speed of 10 m s^{-1} collides with sphere B of mass 1 kg travelling in the same direction at a speed of 4 m s^{-1}. If the speed of A after the collision is v_A and the speed of B after the collision is v_B, and the coefficient of restitution between A and B is 0.4, find the values of v_A and v_B.

Answer

②

$10 \text{ms}^{-1} \longrightarrow \qquad\qquad 4 \text{ms}^{-1} \longrightarrow$

A 2 kg $\qquad\qquad$ B 1kg

$\longrightarrow v_A \qquad\qquad \longrightarrow v_B$

Applying conservation of momentum, we obtain

$$(2 \times 10) + (1 \times 4) = 2v_A + v_B$$

$$24 = 2v_A + v_B \qquad\qquad (1)$$

Applying Newton's law of restitution, we obtain

$$v_B - v_A = -0.4(4 - 10)$$

$$v_B - v_A = 2.4 \qquad\qquad (2)$$

> The numbers are substituted into the equation
>
> $v_B - v_A = -e(u_B - u_A)$

Multiplying equation (2) by 2, we obtain

$$2v_B - 2v_A = 4.8$$

Adding this equation to equation (1), we obtain

$$28.8 = 3v_B$$

Hence $\qquad\qquad v_B = 9.6 \text{ m s}^{-1}$

Substituting this value into equation (1), we obtain

$$24 = 2v_A + 9.6$$

Hence $\qquad\qquad v_A = 7.2 \text{ m s}^{-1}$

3 A sphere A, of mass 4 kg, moving with speed 3 m s^{-1} on a smooth horizontal table collides directly with another sphere B, of mass 5 kg, moving in the opposite direction with speed 2 m s^{-1}. The coefficient of restitution between the spheres is 0.2.

(a) Calculate the speed of A and the speed of B after the collision. [7]

After the collision, sphere B collides directly with a vertical wall. The coefficient of restitution between B and the wall is 0.6.

(b) Find the magnitude of the impulse exerted on B by the wall. [4]

(WJEC M1 Jan 2012 Q2)

Answer

③ (a)

> The negative sign in -2 m s^{-1} indicates B is moving to the left.

Applying conservation of momentum, we obtain

$$(4 \times 3) - (5 \times 2) = 4v_A + 5v_B$$

$$2 = 4v_A + 5v_B \tag{1}$$

Applying Newton's law of restitution, we obtain

$$v_B - v_A = -0.2(-2 - 3)$$

$$v_B - v_A = 1 \tag{2}$$

Multiplying equation (2) by 4, we obtain

$$4v_B - 4v_A = 4$$

Adding this equation to equation (1), we obtain

$$9v_B = 6$$

Hence $\qquad v_B = \dfrac{6}{9} = \dfrac{2}{3}$ or 0.6667 m s^{-1}

and $\qquad v_A = v_B - 1$ from equation (2)

$$= 0.6667 - 1$$

$$= -0.3333 \text{ m s}^{-1}$$

(b) $\qquad$ Impulse $= m(v - u)$

$$= 5(v - 0.6667) \tag{1}$$

Now, $\qquad e = \dfrac{v}{u}$

$$0.6 = \dfrac{v}{0.6667}$$

Hence $\qquad v = 0.4$ m s^{-1}

> u is the speed before hitting the wall and v the speed after hitting the wall.

$v = -0.4$ as it is in the opposite direction to u. It is important to note that in the equation $e = \dfrac{v}{u}$, v and u are speeds. It may therefore be necessary to make v negative before putting it into another equation as is the case here.

> Because we have used the change in momentum of the sphere this will be the impulse of the wall exerted on the sphere.

Substituting this value of v into equation (1), we obtain

$$\text{Impulse} = 5(-0.4 - 0.6667)$$

$$= -5.3335 \text{ N s}$$

Magnitude of the impulse exerted on B
by the wall $= 5.3335$ N s

> Note that the alternative units for impulse of kg m s^{-1} could be used here.

❹ A particle A, of mass 2 kg, moving with speed 12 m s^{-1} on a smooth horizontal surface collides directly with a particle B, of mass 3 kg, moving with speed 7 m s^{-1} in the same direction as A. The coefficient of restitution between the particles is 0.6.

(a) Find the speeds of A and B after the collision. [7]

(b) Find the magnitude of the impulse exerted by A on B during the collision. [2]

(WJEC M1 June 2010 Q4)

Answer

④ (a)

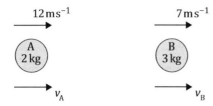

Applying conservation of momentum, we obtain

$(2 \times 12) + (3 \times 7) = 2v_A + 3v_B$

$45 = 2v_A + 3v_B$ (1)

Applying Newton's law of restitution, we obtain

$v_B - v_A = -0.6(7 - 12)$

$v_B - v_A = 3$ (2)

> Note that both particles are moving to the right before the collision.

Multiplying equation (2) by 3, we obtain

$3v_B - 3v_A = 9$

Subtracting the above equation from equation (1), we obtain

$36 = 5v_A$

$v_A = 7.2$ m s^{-1}

Substituting this value into equation (2) gives $v_B = 10.2$ m s^{-1}

(b) Impulse = change in momentum

$I = m(v - u)$

$I = 3(10.2 - 7)$

$= 9.6$ N s

⌃⌃ Grade boost

You may be penalised if you do not include the correct units for the impulse. Units should always be included unless you are asked to determine the coefficient of restitution which has no units.

❺ An object A, of mass 3 kg, moving with speed 7 m s^{-1} on a smooth horizontal plane collides directly with another object B, of mass 5 kg, moving with speed 3 m s^{-1} in the **opposite** direction. After the collision, the direction of motion of B is reversed and its speed is 2.4 m s^{-1}.

(a) Calculate the coefficient of restitution between A and B. [6]

After the collision between A and B, the object B collides with a wall which is perpendicular to its direction of motion. The coefficient of restitution between the wall and B is 0.6.

(b) Calculate the speed of B after the collision with the wall. [2]

(WJEC M1 Jan 2010 Q7)

Answer

⑤ (a)

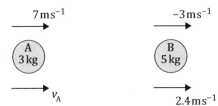

Applying conservation of momentum, we obtain

$$(3 \times 7) + (5 \times (-3)) = 3v_A + (5 \times 2.4)$$
$$6 = 3v_A + 12$$

Hence $\qquad v_A = -2 \text{ m s}^{-1}$

Applying Newton's law of restitution, we obtain

$$v_B - v_A = -e(u_B - u_A)$$
$$2.4 - (-2) = -e(-3 - 7)$$
$$4.4 = e(10)$$

Hence coefficient of restitution, $e = 0.44$

> Note again that the negative sign in -3 m s^{-1} indicates that B is moving to the left.

(b)

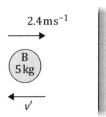

Let v' be the speed of B after the collision with the wall

Applying Newton's law of restitution, we obtain

$$v' = 0.6 \times 2.4$$

Hence $\qquad v' = 1.44 \text{ m s}^{-1}$

Hence speed after collision with wall = 1.44 m s^{-1}

> The formula for the collision of a particle with a perpendicular wall is used here. The formula is
> $$e = \frac{v}{u}.$$

Examination style question

❶ A particle A, of mass 0.3 kg, moving with speed 3 m s^{-1} on a smooth horizontal surface collides directly with a particle B, of mass 0.2 kg, moving with speed 2 m s^{-1} in the opposite direction. The coefficient of restitution between the particles is 0.8.

(a) Find the speeds of A and B after the collision. [7]

(b) After the collision with particle A, particle B then goes on to collide with a fixed smooth vertical wall which is at right angles to the path of the particle. If the coefficient of restitution between particle B and the wall is 0.7, find the speed of particle B after its collision with the wall. [3]

Answer

① (a)

Applying conservation of momentum, we obtain

$$(0.3 \times 3) + (0.2 \times (-2)) = 0.3v_A + 0.2v_B$$

$$0.5 = 0.3v_A + 0.2v_B$$

Multiplying both sides of this equation by 10, we obtain

$$5 = 3v_A + 2v_B \qquad (1)$$

Applying Newton's law of restitution, we obtain

$$v_B - v_A = -e(u_B - u_A)$$

$$v_B - v_A = -0.8(-2 - 3)$$

$$v_B - v_A = 4 \qquad (2)$$

Multiplying equation (2) by 2, we obtain

$$2v_B - 2v_A = 8$$

Subtracting this equation from equation (1) gives

$$5v_A = -3$$

Hence $\qquad v_A = -0.6$ m s^{-1}

Substituting $v_A = -0.6$ m s^{-1} into equation (1), we obtain

$$5 = 3(-0.6) + 2v_B$$

Hence $\qquad v_B = 3.4$ m s^{-1}

> Make sure you check the answers from the simultaneous equations. In the way worked out here, you would substitute both answers into equation (2) and ensure that the left-hand side of the equation equals the right-hand side. You should also substitute both answers into equation (1) as an extra check.

(b) For an object bouncing off a perpendicular wall:

$$e = \frac{v}{u}$$

Hence putting the values into this equation

we have, $\qquad 0.7 = \dfrac{v}{3.4}$

> Only put the magnitude of v and u into this equation.

Hence speed of B after the collision with the wall, $v = 2.38$ m s^{-1}

Test yourself

1 A steel ball A of mass 3 kg and speed 5 m s^{-1} moves along a smooth horizontal surface where it hits another steel ball B of mass 4 kg which is at rest on the surface.

After the collision, ball A is at rest whilst ball B moves away from A. Find the speed of ball B.

2 Two toy cars are moving in the same direction. Car A of mass 0.2 kg travelling with a speed of 0.1 m s^{-1}, collides with car B of mass 0.1 kg travelling with a speed of 0.05 m s^{-1}. After the collision, car A continues to move in the same direction this time with a reduced speed of 0.08 m s^{-1}.

(a) Find the speed of car B after the collision.

(b) Calculate the coefficient of restitution between the cars.

3 A ball of mass 0.5 kg travelling in a horizontal straight line with a speed of 4 m s^{-1} hits a fixed vertical wall and rebounds from it with speed of 3 m s^{-1}. Find the magnitude of the impulse exerted on the wall by the ball.

4 Particle P of mass 3 kg and speed 6 m s^{-1} moves across a smooth horizontal surface in a straight line. A particle Q has a mass of 4 kg and is at rest on the surface.

Particle P collides with particle Q.

(a) If, after the collision, P is at rest and Q moves away from P, find the speed of Q.

(b) Calculate the coefficient of restitution between the particles.

1   A sphere A, of mass 3 kg, moving with speed 8 m s^{-1} on a smooth horizontal plane, collides directly with another sphere B, of mass 7 kg, moving with speed 5 m s^{-1} on the plane in the same direction. The coefficient of restitution between the spheres is 0.4.

(a)   Calculate the speed of A and the speed of B immediately after the collision.   *[7]*

(b)   Find the impulse exerted by A on B.   *[2]*

(WJEC M1 Jan 2011 Q4)

Answer

1   (a)

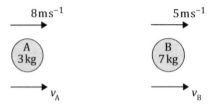

Applying conservation of momentum, we obtain

$$(3 \times 8) + (7 \times 5) = 3v_A + 7v_B$$

$$59 = 3v_A + 7v_B \qquad (1)$$

Applying Newton's law of restitution, we obtain

$$v_B - v_A = -0.4(5 - 8)$$

$$v_B - v_A = 1.2 \qquad (2)$$

Multiplying equation (2) by 7, we obtain

$$7v_B - 7v_A = 8.4$$

Subtracting this equation from equation (1) we obtain

$$10v_A = 50.6$$

$$v_A = 5.06 \text{ m s}^{-1}$$

Substituting $v_A = 5.06$ into equation (2) gives

$$v_B - 5.06 = 1.2$$

$$v_B = 6.26 \text{ m s}^{-1}$$

The equation
$$v_B - v_A = -e(u_B - u_A)$$
is used here.

(b)   Impulse exerted by A on B = change in momentum of B.

$$= 7(6.26 - 5)$$

$$= 8.82 \text{ N s}$$

2   Two particles A and B are sliding **towards** each other on a smooth horizontal surface and collide directly. Particle A has mass 3 kg and particle B has mass 4 kg. Just before the collision, A has speed 5 m s^{-1} and B has speed 3 m s^{-1}.

Immediately after the collision, A has reversed its direction of motion and its speed is 2 m s^{-1}.

(a) Show that the speed of B immediately after the collision is 2.25 m s^{-1}.   [3]

(b) Find the coefficient of restitution between A and B.   [3]

(c) Determine the magnitude of the impulse exerted by A on B during the collision.   [2]

(WJEC M1 June 2011 Q7)

Answer

2   (a)

5ms^{-1} -3ms^{-1}

A
3 kg

B
4 kg

-2ms^{-1} v_B

Applying conservation of momentum, we have

$(3 \times 5) + (4 \times (-3)) = (3 \times (-2)) + 4v_B$

giving $v_B = 2.25 \text{ m s}^{-1}$

(b) $-e = \dfrac{v_B - v_A}{u_B - u_A} = \dfrac{2.25 - (-2)}{-3 - 5} = -\dfrac{4.25}{8} = -0.53125$

Hence coefficient of restitution, $e = 0.53125$ or 0.53 (correct to two decimal places)

(c)   For impulse of A on B, we obtain

$$I = m(v - u)$$
$$= 4(2.25 - (-3))$$
$$= 21 \text{ N s}$$

Magnitude of the impulse = 21 N s

Summary: Momentum and impulse

Momentum

Momentum = mass × velocity measured in the units of kg m s^{-1}

Momentum is a vector quantity so it has magnitude and direction.

Impulse

If a constant force F acts on a body for a time t seconds, then the impulse I of the force is given by the equation:

Impulse = force × time (or = Ft)

The units of impulse are N s or kg m s^{-1}.

Also, impulse I = Change in momentum

I = final momentum − initial momentum

$I = mv - mu$

$I = m(v - u)$

u is the initial velocity

v is the final velocity

m is the mass.

Conservation of momentum

The law of conservation of momentum

Total momentum before a collision = total momentum after the collision (provided that no external forces act).

$$m_A u_A + m_B u_B = m_A v_A + m_B v_B$$

Newton's experimental law for the direct impact of two bodies moving in the same straight line

u_A = initial velocity of mass A

u_B = initial velocity of mass B

v_A = final velocity of mass A

v_B = final velocity of mass B

e = coefficient of restitution

$$\frac{v_B - v_A}{u_B - u_A} = -e \qquad \text{or} \qquad v_B - v_A = -e(u_B - u_A)$$

Newton's experimental law for the impact of a body moving at right angles to a plane

For an object bouncing off a plane at right angles to its path such as a wall:

$$e = \frac{v}{u}$$

e = coefficient of restitution between the object and the wall

v = speed of the object after impact

u = speed of the object before impact

Topic 5 Statics

This topic covers the following:

- Composition and resolution of forces
- Equilibrium of a particle under the action of coplanar forces
- The moment of a force about a point
- Equilibrium of a rigid body under the action of parallel coplanar forces
- Centre of mass of uniform laminae (triangles, rectangles, circles and composite shapes)
- Equilibrium of a plane lamina or a coplanar system of particles connected by light rods

Composition and resolution of forces

Resolution of forces

A force F can be replaced by a pair of forces, called the components of F, with both of these components acting at right angles to each other as shown in the following diagram:

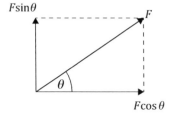

One component acts at an angle θ to the original force and has a size of $F\cos\theta$ and the other force acts at right angles to this component and has a size of $F\sin\theta$.

Sometimes you will be asked to find the resultant force, F, of two forces acting at right angles to each other and this is how to do it:

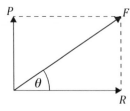

The size of the resultant force, F, is found by using Pythagoras' theorem, so we have

$$F^2 = P^2 + R^2$$

The direction of F can be referenced using the angle θ measured to the horizontal.

The angle θ can be found using

$$\tan\theta = \frac{P}{R} \qquad \text{so} \qquad \theta = \tan^{-1}\left(\frac{P}{R}\right)$$

Composition of forces

Composition of forces is finding a single force which is equivalent to two or more given forces acting in given directions.

Here is an example. You are asked to find the single force that would replace the three forces shown in the diagram.

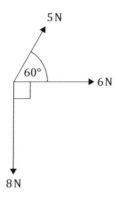

You can see from the diagram that the component of the 5 N force in the horizontal direction will add to the 6 N force. The vertical component of the 5 N force will be unable to balance the larger 8 N force acting down so the net force in this direction will be downwards.

Component of the 5 N force in the horizontal direction = 5 cos 60° = 2.5 N

Resolving horizontally we obtain, net resultant force = 6 + 2.5 = 8.5 N (to the right)

Component of the 5 N force in the vertical direction = 5 sin 60° = 4.3301 N

Resolving vertically, we obtain, net resultant force = 8 − 4.3301 = 3.6699 N (downwards)

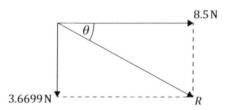

Remember that the two forces are at right angles to each other so Pythagoras' theorem and trigonometry can be used to work out lengths of sides and angles.

Resultant force R is found using Pythagoras' theorem:

$R^2 = 8.5^2 + 3.6699^2$

giving $R = 9.2584$ N.

$$\theta = \tan^{-1}\left(\frac{3.6699}{8.5}\right) = 23.4° \text{ (to the horizontal)}$$

You will not be given Pythagoras' theorem or the trigonometric ratios, so you will need to remember them.

Equilibrium of a particle under the action of coplanar forces

A particle is said to be in equilibrium under the action of two or more forces, if the particle remains stationary. You saw in Topic 2 that unbalanced forces produce a net or resultant force that causes a particle to be accelerated. When a particle is in equilibrium there is no resultant force and therefore no acceleration.

To solve a problem involving particles in equilibrium there are a number of steps to take:

- Draw an accurate diagram (if one is not already provided) and mark on all the forces acting.
- Resolve all the forces into vertical and horizontal components when they act at an angle.
- Equate to zero all the vertical forces acting.
- Equate to zero all the horizontal forces acting.
- Solve these equations to find the unknown forces or angles.

Examples

❶ The particle in the diagram is in equilibrium under the action of three forces.

Resolve horizontally and vertically to find the size of forces P and R correct to two decimal places.

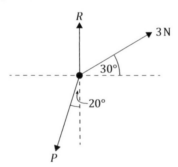

Answer

① Resolving horizontally, we obtain

$$3 \cos 30° - P \sin 20° = 0$$

Hence
$$P = \frac{3 \cos 30°}{\sin 20°} = 7.5963 \text{ N}$$

$$P = 7.60 \text{ N (correct to two decimal places)}$$

Resolving vertically, we obtain

$$R + 3 \sin 30° - P \cos 20° = 0$$

$$R + 1.5 - 7.5963 \cos 20° = 0$$

$$R = 5.6382 \text{ N}$$

$$R = 5.64 \text{ N (correct to two decimal places)}$$

Here we have taken forces to the right and upward forces as being in the positive direction. Alternatively, you can just equate the upward and downward forces and also equate the forces to the right with the forces to the left.

Note that we have only been asked to find the size of the force and not its direction as well.

2 The diagram shows four horizontal forces acting at a point O. The forces are in equilibrium. Calculate the value of P and the size of the angle θ. Give each of your answers correct to one decimal place. *[8]*

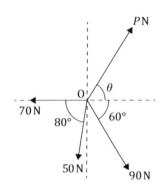

(WJEC M1 Jan 2011 Q5)

Answer

② Resolving horizontally, and equating left and right forces, we obtain

$$P\cos\theta + 90\cos 60° = 70 + 50\cos 80°$$

Hence $\qquad\qquad P\cos\theta = 33.6824$ (1)

> Do not round your intermediate answers off to one decimal place. Only round off your final answers.

Resolving vertically, we obtain

$$P\sin\theta = 90\sin 60° + 50\sin 80°$$

Hence $\qquad\qquad P\sin\theta = 127.1827$ (2)

Dividing equation (2) by equation (1) gives

$$\tan\theta = \frac{127.1827}{33.6824} = 3.7759$$

> Remember that
> $$\frac{\sin\theta}{\cos\theta} = \tan\theta$$

Hence $\qquad\qquad \theta = 75.1666°$

So $\theta = 75.2°$ correct to one decimal place

Squaring equations (1) and (2) and then adding them together, we obtain

$$P^2\sin^2\theta + P^2\cos^2\theta = 127.1827^2 + 33.6824^2$$

$$P^2(\sin^2\theta + \cos^2\theta) = 127.1827^2 + 33.6824^2$$

$$P^2 = 127.1827^2 + 33.6824^2$$

> Here we use the result
> $$\sin^2\theta + \cos^2\theta = 1$$

Hence $\qquad\qquad P = 131.6$ N (correct to one decimal place)

3 A particle P lies on a horizontal plane. Three horizontal forces of magnitude 7 N, 12 N and 16 N acting in directions as shown in the diagram are applied to P.

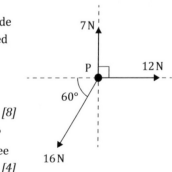

(a) Show that the magnitude of the resultant of the three forces is approximately 7.9 N. Find the angle between the direction of the resultant and the direction of the 12 N force. *[8]*

(b) The particle P has mass 5 kg and the coefficient of friction between P and the plane is 0.1. Taking the magnitude of the resultant of the three forces to be 7.9 N, calculate the magnitude of the acceleration of P. *[4]*

(WJEC M1 Jan 2012 Q6)

Answer

③ (a) Component of the 16 N force in the opposite direction to the 12 N force
$$= 16 \cos 60° = 8 \text{ N (to the left)}$$

Net resultant force $= 12 - 8 = 4$ N   (to the right in the direction of the original 12 N force)

Component of the 16 N force acting in the opposite direction to the 7 N force
$$= 16 \sin 60° = 13.8564 \text{ N}$$

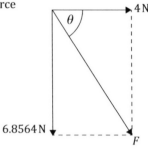

Net resultant vertical force $= 13.8564 - 7 = 6.8564$ N

Resultant force F is found using Pythagoras' theorem
$$F^2 = 4^2 + 6.8564^2$$

giving $F = 7.9379$ N $= 7.9$ (correct to one decimal place)

$$\theta = \tan^{-1}\left(\frac{6.8564}{4}\right) = 59.7° \text{ (to the direction of the 12 N force)}$$

(b)

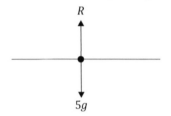

R and $5\,g$ act in the vertical direction.

The normal reaction is $5g$ (i.e. equal to the weight). All the other forces act in the horizontal plane.

The maximum frictional force depends on the normal reaction of the plane on the particle.

Resolving vertically, we have
$$R = 5g$$

Solving gives $R = 49$ N

The driving horizontal force on the particle is the resultant found in part (a), i.e. 7.9 N, which is directly opposed by the maximum frictional force
$$\mu R = 0.1 \times 49 = 4.9 \text{ N}$$

Then, applying Newton's second law to the particle in a horizontal direction, we have
$$5a = 7.9 - 4.9$$

giving $a = 0.6 \text{ m s}^{-2}$

The moment of a force about a point

A moment is the turning effect of a force. The moment of a force about a point P is the product of the magnitude of the force and the perpendicular distance of the line of action of the force from the point P.

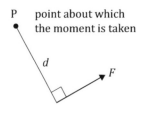

P — point about which the moment is taken

d

F

Moment = Force × Distance

This is an anticlockwise moment as it produces an anticlockwise turning effect. The units of moments are N m.

Note that the distance must be the perpendicular distance from the point about which moments are taken to the line of action of the force.

Moments can be either clockwise or anticlockwise depending on the direction of the turning effect they produce. We take one direction (usually clockwise) to be positive and the other direction to be negative. Moments are taken about a point to find the sizes of forces or their distances to a certain point by using the following principle of moments:

When a body is in equilibrium, the sum of the clockwise moments is equal to the sum of the anticlockwise moments.

Equilibrium of a rigid body under the action of parallel coplanar forces

If a rigid body, such as a rod, under the action of parallel coplanar forces is in equilibrium then the following is true:

1. The resultant force in any direction is zero.

2. The sum of the moments about any point is zero.

Examples

❶ The diagram shows a uniform rod AB of length 2 m and mass 10 kg. The rod is resting horizontally in equilibrium on two supports, one at point A and the other at C where AC = 1.5 m.

A ——————————————— C ——— B

Calculate the reactions at A and C.

Answer

①

R_1 1.5 m R_2 0.5 m

A   1 m   C   B

$10g$

Draw an accurate diagram marking all the forces acting along with the distances given in the question.

As the rod is uniform, the weight of the rod $10g$ may be supposed to act downwards at the centre of the rod.

As the rod is in equilibrium, resolving vertically, we obtain

$$R_1 + R_2 = 10g \quad\quad (1)$$

Taking moments about point A, we obtain

$$10g \times 1 = R_2 \times 1.5$$

$$R_2 = 65.33 \text{ N}$$

Substituting this value of R_2 into equation (1) we obtain

$$R_1 + 65.33 = 10 \times 9.8$$

$$R_1 = 32.67 \text{ N}$$

> The total of the upwards forces will equal the total of the downward forces.

> Point A is chosen because R_1 acts through A and will have no moment about A (i.e. because its distance to A is zero). Using this point, we can find R_2 easily. Note that anticlockwise and clockwise moments are equal.

❷ A uniform rod AB is suspended horizontally from the ceiling by means of two vertical light inextensible strings XA and YB of equal length.

The rod AB has mass 6 kg and length 1.4 m. A particle, of mass 10 kg, is attached to the rod at point C, where AC = 0.3 m. Calculate the tension in **each** of the strings XA and YB. [7]

(WJEC M1 June 2010 Q7)

Answer

②

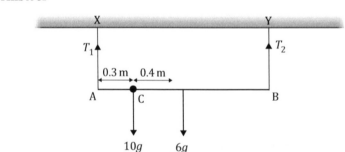

> The tensions in the strings are not the same and they act vertically upwards on the rod.

Let the tension in string YB = T_2

Taking moments about point A, we have

$$T_2 \times 1.4 = (6 \times 9.8 \times 0.7) + (10 \times 9.8 \times 0.3)$$

giving $\quad\quad T_2 = 50.4 \text{ N}$

Let the tension in string XA = T_1

Distance CB = 1.4 − 0.3 = 1.1

Taking moments about point B, we have

$$T_1 \times 1.4 = (6 \times 9.8 \times 0.7) + (10 \times 9.8 \times 1.1)$$

giving $\quad\quad T_1 = 106.4 \text{ N}$

> The choice of A is made because T_1 has no moment about A.

> You could alternatively have resolved vertically to obtain an equation containing both T_1 and T_2. The value of T_2 could be substituted into this equation to find T_1.

❸ The diagram shows a body, of mass 65 kg, attached to the end B of a uniform rigid rod AB of length 4 m. The mass of the rod is 35 kg. The rod is held horizontally in equilibrium by two smooth cylindrical pegs, one at A and another at C, where AC = 1.2 m.

(a) Write down the moment of the weight of the rod about the point A. State your units clearly.   *[2]*

(b) Find the forces exerted on the rod at A and C.   *[6]*

(WJEC M1 Jan 2012 Q7)

Answer

③ (a)

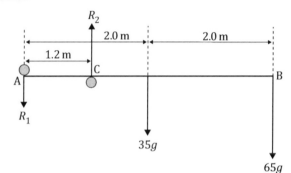

> To decide on the directions of the reactions R_1 and R_2 think about the forces exerted by the rod on the pegs A and C which will be upwards and downwards respectively. The forces on the rod are in an opposite direction according to Newton's third law.

Moment of the weight about $A = F \times d$

$$= 35g \times 2$$

$$= 686 \text{ N m (in a clockwise direction)}$$

(b) As the rod is in equilibrium, resolving vertically, we obtain

$$R_2 = R_1 + 35g + 65g$$

$$R_2 = R_1 + 100g \qquad (1)$$

Taking moments about A, we obtain

$$R_2 \times 1.2 = 686 + 65g \times 4$$

Hence $R_2 = 2695 \text{ N}$

Substituting this value of R_2 into equation (1), we obtain

$$2695 = R_1 + 980$$

Hence $R_1 = 1715 \text{ N}$

❹ A uniform rod AB, of mass 3 kg, has length 2 m. A particle of mass 5 kg is attached to the end A, and a particle of mass 2 kg is attached to the end B. The diagram shows the rod resting horizontally in equilibrium on a smooth support at the point C, where AC = x m.

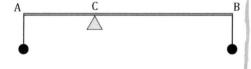

Calculate the magnitude of the reaction of the support at C and the value of x.   *[6]*

(WJEC M1 Jan 2011 Q7)

Answer

④

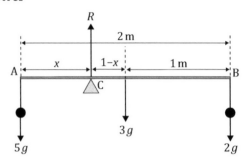

Resolving vertically we obtain

$$R = 5g + 3g + 2g$$
$$R = 10g$$
$$R = 98\,\text{N}$$

As the rod is in equilibrium, the upward force must equal the sum of the downward forces.

Taking moments about the pivot C

$$5gx = 3g(1 - x) + 2g(2 - x)$$
$$10x = 7$$
$$x = 0.7\,\text{m}$$

You can take moments about any point provided that all the distances from the forces to the point are known. Taking moments about the pivot is an obvious choice here especially as force R has no moment about the pivot.

Centre of mass of uniform laminae (triangles, rectangles, circles and composite shapes)

The centre of mass of a uniform lamina is the point at which the entire mass is assumed to be situated.

If a lamina is freely suspended from any point, then it will rest so that the line between the point of suspension and the centre of mass is vertical.

Centre of mass of a rectangle – situated where the lines joining the mid-points of the sides intersect.

Centre of mass of a circle – situated at the centre of the circle.

Centre of mass of a triangle – situated on the median (i.e. a line joining the vertex of the triangle to the mid-point of the base).

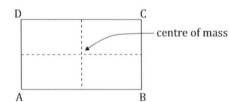

The following formula is used to work out where the mid-point lies on the median:

Centre of mass for a triangular lamina is $\frac{2}{3}$ along median from vertex

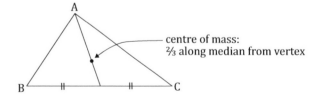

The formula for the centre of mass for a triangle is given in the formula booklet. For all the other shapes, you will need to remember where the centre of mass is situated.

Many of the questions on centre of mass involve finding the centre of mass for a right-angled triangle. The centre of mass of a right-angled triangle is situated one-third of the way out from the right angle along both sides or two-thirds from a vertex towards the right angle.

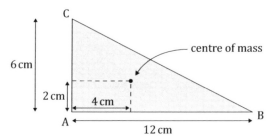

The centre of mass is located one-third of the way along the two sides which are at right angles to each other. Note that this only applies to a right-angled triangle.

Finding the centre of mass of composite shapes

Sometimes, it is necessary to find the centre of mass of a lamina which is constructed by combining shapes such as rectangles and triangles, amongst others. Thus, for example, we may wish to find the centre of mass of the lamina shown below, which consists of a rectangle and a triangle.

The diagram below shows a uniform lamina (a thin piece of cardboard, metal, etc.) formed by attaching a right-angled triangle to a rectangle. Shapes made up from either adding or taking away other shapes are called composite shapes.

In order to find the position of the centre of mass of the lamina we need to take the following steps:

1 Find the area of each shape.

2 Find the area of the lamina by either adding or taking away the areas of the shapes making up the lamina.

3 Find the distance of the centres of mass of each of the shapes from a horizontal line or axis and also the distance from a vertical line or axis.

4 Put the information gained in a table as the following example shows.

5 Find the moments of the shapes that form the lamina and add or subtract them depending on whether their areas add to the lamina or subtract from it. The moment for each shape is found by multiplying the area of the shape by its distance to either a vertical or horizontal line/axis; the distances of the centre of mass of the lamina from the vertical and horizontal lines are taken to be x and y respectively.

6 Find the moment of the lamina about each line/axis and equate the moment to those in part 5.

7 Solve the two equations for x and y to find the distances to the lines.

The following example will be used to explain the above processes.

Here we are asked to find the centre of mass of the uniform lamina shown formed by adding a right-angled triangle to a rectangle. We are asked to find the centre of mass from the lines AB and AE.

We are able to use our knowledge of the areas of rectangles and triangles, together with information concerning the positions of their centres of mass, to find the position of the centre of mass of the composite lamina.

In essence, the method is as follows:

(a) draw up a table listing all information concerning the various shapes (areas and positions of centres of mass)

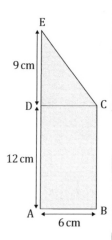

(b) use the principle of moments, namely

Moment of the area of the composite lamina = sum of the moments of the component areas making up the composite lamina

We will illustrate the process of finding the centre of mass of the uniform lamina given here.

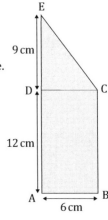

(a) Drawing up the table

Shape	Area of shape	Distance of centre of mass from AE	Distance of centre of mass from AB
Triangle CDE	$\frac{1}{2} \times 6 \times 9 = 27$	$\frac{1}{3} \times 6 = 2$	$\left(\frac{1}{3} \times 9\right) + 12 = 15$
Rectangle ABCD	$6 \times 12 = 72$	$\frac{1}{2} \times 6 = 3$	$\frac{1}{2} \times 12 = 6$
Lamina ABCDE	$27 + 72 = 99$	x	y

Notes on the table

(i)   The sides AB and AE have been used as reference axes.

(ii) The centre of mass position is characterised by the unknown distances x and y (to be determined).

(b) Principle of moments

The general principle is:

$$\begin{array}{ccc} \text{Moment of area of} & & \text{Moment of area of} \qquad \text{Moment of area of} \\ \text{lamina ABCDE} & = & \text{triangle CDE} \quad + \quad \text{rectangle ABCD} \end{array}$$

Moments about AE

$$99x = (72 \times 3) + (27 \times 2)$$

giving $x = 2.7$ cm (correct to one decimal place)

Moments about AB

$$99y = (72 \times 6) + (27 \times 15)$$

giving $y = 8.5$ cm (correct to one decimal place)

> The moment of a shape is its area multiplied by the distance to the line about which moments are taken.

Equilibrium of a plane lamina

Once the centre of mass of a lamina has been found it can be used to find how the lamina will lie when freely suspended from a certain point.

When a lamina is freely suspended, it will lie so that its centre of mass lies vertically below the point of suspension. This is best understood by following carefully the next example.

Example

❶ The diagram shows a uniform lamina formed by removing a circle, of radius 3 cm, from a rectangular card ABCD where AB = 10 cm and BC = 12 cm. The centre of the circle is 7 cm from AB and 4 cm from AD.

(a) Calculate the distances of the centre of mass of the lamina from AD and AB.

Give your answers correct to three decimal places. [9]

(b) The lamina is freely suspended from A and hangs in equilibrium.

Calculate the angle AB makes with the vertical. [3]

(c) When the lamina is suspended freely from a point P on DC, it hangs with AD vertical.

Write down the value of DP. [1]

(WJEC M1 Jan 2011 Q8)

Answer

(a)

Shape	Area of shape	Distance of centre of mass from AD	Distance of centre of mass from AB
Rectangle ABCD	120	5	6
Circle	9π	4	7
Lamina	$120 - 9\pi$	x	y

Taking moments about AD, we have

$$120 \times 5 = (9\pi \times 4) + (120 - 9\pi) \times x$$

giving $x = 5.308$ cm

> Moment of complete rectangle = sum of the moments of the circle and lamina.

Taking moments about AB, we have

$$120 \times 6 = (9\pi \times 7) + (120 - 9\pi) \times y$$

giving $y = 5.692$ cm (correct to three decimal places)

(b)

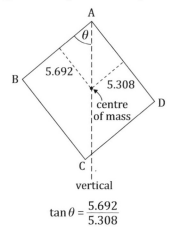

> A vertical line drawn through the point of suspension (i.e. A in this case) will pass through the centre of mass. The distances can be marked on a diagram and are used to calculate the angle θ.

$$\tan \theta = \frac{5.692}{5.308}$$

$\theta = 47.0°$ (correct to one decimal place)

(c)

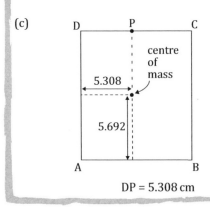

DP = 5.308 cm

It is essential to draw a quick sketch of the arrangement and it is then easy to see the distance required.

Equilibrium of a coplanar system of particles connected by light rods

When a series of particles is connected by light rods, the rods themselves are considered to have zero mass. The mass of each particle is recorded along with the distance to a vertical and horizontal line (usually the x and y axes). Moments can then be taken about each line/axis as the following example shows. As with a uniform lamina, a system of coplanar particles will lie with their centre of mass vertically below the point of suspension.

Example

❶ The diagram below shows four particles A, B, C and D, of mass 8 kg, 4 kg, 5 kg and 2 kg respectively, attached to light rods which are rigidly joined together. The positions of the particles A, B, C and D, on the x–y plane are $(5, 0)$, $(3, 10)$, $(-4, 9)$ and $(-6, 2)$.

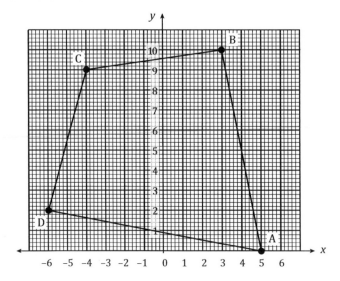

Find the coordinates of the centre of mass of the system.

Answer

①

Mass	x	y
8	5	0
4	3	10
5	−4	9
2	−6	2

Taking moments about the y-axis, we obtain

$$19X = (8 \times 5) + (4 \times 3) + (5 \times (-4)) + (2 \times (-6))$$

Solving, gives X = 1.05

Taking moments about the x-axis, we obtain

$$19Y = (8 \times 0) + (4 \times 10) + (5 \times 9) + (2 \times 2)$$

Solving, gives Y = 4.68

The mass of the particle and its x and y coordinates are recorded in the table.

X and Y are used to denote coordinates of centre of mass of the system.

Note that the total mass of the whole system is 19 kg.

The moment on the left of the equation is the total mass of the system multiplied by the unknown distance to the axis. On the right of the equation is the product of the various masses and their distances to the axis about which the moments are taken.

Examination style questions

1 The diagram shows a uniform lamina consisting of a triangle ABC with a square DEFG removed. The triangle ABC has a right angle at A and the dimensions are marked on the diagram.

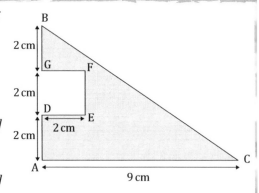

(a) Calculate the distance of the centre of mass of the lamina from AB and AC giving your answer correct to two significant figures. *[7]*

(b) The lamina is freely suspended from A and hangs in equilibrium. Calculate the angle AC makes with the vertical. *[4]*

Answer

① (a)

Shape	Area of shape	Distance of centre of mass from AB	Distance of centre of mass from AC
Triangle ABC	27	3	2
Square DEFG	4	1	3
Lamina	23	x	y

Taking moments about AB, we have

$$23x = (27 \times 3) - (4 \times 1)$$

Giving $x = 3.3478 \text{ cm}$

$x = 3.3 \text{ cm}$ (correct to two significant figures)

Taking moments about AC, we have

$$23y = (27 \times 2) - (4 \times 3)$$

Giving $y = 1.8261 \text{ cm}$

$y = 1.8 \text{ cm}$ (correct to two significant figures)

> As the square is removed, its area must be subtracted to find the area of the lamina. Also, the moment of the area of the square must be subtracted from the moment of the area of the rectangle.

> Always give your answer to the number of significant figures or decimal places specified in the question, if they are given.

(b) When suspended from A, the centre of mass, M, will lie vertically below A.

The angle θ will be the angle the side AC makes with the vertical.

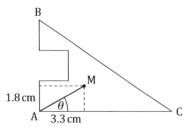

> Remember that the centre of mass will always lie vertically below the point of suspension.

$$\theta = \tan^{-1}\left(\frac{1.8261}{3.3478}\right)$$

$$\theta = 28.6° \text{ (correct to one decimal place)}$$

❷ The diagram shows a uniform straight rod of length 4 m, resting horizontally in equilibrium on two supports at C and D. An object of mass 2.5 kg is suspended from point B.

If the mass of the rod is 5.6 kg and distances AC = 0.6 m and AD = 2.8 m, calculate the magnitudes of the reactions at C and D.

Answer

②

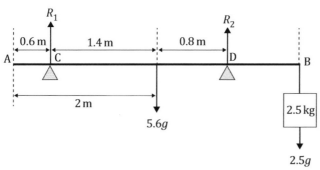

Resolving vertically, we obtain

$$R_1 + R_2 = 5.6g + 2.5g$$
$$R_1 + R_2 = 79.38 \qquad (1)$$

Taking moments about point C, we obtain

$$(5.6g \times 1.4) + (2.5g \times 3.4) = R_2 \times 2.2$$

Solving gives $\qquad R_2 = 72.787 \text{ N}$

Substituting this value for R_2 into equation (1), we obtain

$$R_1 + 72.787 = 79.38$$

Hence $\qquad R_1 = 6.593 \text{ N}$

Test yourself

❶ Three horizontal forces of magnitudes 10 N, 8 N and 6 N act on a particle in the directions shown in the diagram.

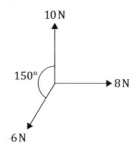

Find the magnitude of the resultant force and the angle between the resultant force and the 8 N force.

❷ The diagram shows a uniform rod AB of length 2 m and mass 4 kg with a particle of mass 0.5 kg attached at A. The rod is resting horizontally in equilibrium on two smooth supports at points P and Q of the rod, where AP = 0.4 m and AQ = 1.4 m.

Calculate the reactions at P and Q.

❸ A uniform rod AB of length 1.8 m and mass 5 kg is suspended horizontally from a rigid horizontal ceiling at points P and Q by two vertical light inextensible strings.

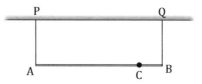

A particle of mass 2 kg is placed on the rod at point C which is 0.2 m from B.

Calculate the tensions in each string.

1 The diagram shows a sign attached to a point A. It is supported by two light rods AB and AC.

The rod AC is horizontal and the rod AB is inclined at an angle of α to the horizontal, where $\sin \alpha = 0.6$.

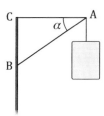

The mass of the sign is 12 kg. Calculate:

(a)   the thrust in the rod AB,   [3]

(b)   the tension in the rod AC.   [3]

(WJEC M1 June 2011 Q4)

Answer

1   **(a)**

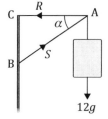   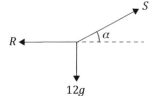

> R is the tension in rod AC and S is the thrust in rod AB.

The forces acting at point A are in equilibrium.

Resolving vertically, we have

$$S \sin \alpha = 12g$$

$$S \times 0.6 = 12 \times 9.8$$

Thrust in AB, $S = 196\,\text{N}$

> Note that if, $\sin \alpha = 0.6$, $\cos \alpha = 0.8$

(b)   Resolving horizontally, we have

$$S \cos \alpha = R$$

Tension in AC, $R = 156.8\,\text{N}$

2 A uniform lamina OAQP is formed by removing the isosceles triangle PQB from the triangle OAB as shown in the diagram below, which is drawn to scale. The triangle OAB is isosceles with OB = AB. The line PQ is parallel to the line OA.

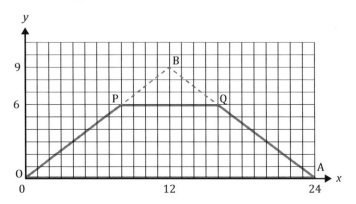

(a) Calculate the coordinates of the centre of mass of the lamina OAQP.   [7]

(b) The lamina is freely suspended from P and hangs in equilibrium.

     Calculate the angle PQ makes with the vertical.   [3]

(WJEC M1 June 2011 Q9)

Answer

2 (a)

Shape	Area of shape	Distance of centre of mass from Oy	Distance of centre of mass from Ox
Triangle OAB	$\frac{1}{2} \times 24 \times 9 = 108$	12	$\frac{1}{3} \times 9 = 3$
Triangle PQB	$\frac{1}{2} \times 8 \times 3 = 12$	12	7
Lamina	$108 - 12 = 96$	x	y

The x-coordinate of the centre of mass of shape = 12 (as both triangles have a centre of mass lying somewhere along the line $x = 12$).

Taking moments about Ox, we obtain

Moment of OAQP = moment of OAB

　　　　　　　　　　　 − moment of PQB

$$96y = (108 \times 3) - (12 \times 7)$$

giving, y-coordinate, $y = 2.5$

Hence the coordinates of the centre of mass are (12, 2.5).

 Grade boost

Look at the given diagram carefully. You have to look at the shape in terms of centres of masses of shapes which are known. The centre of mass for a triangular lamina is given in the formula booklet. You need to think of this shape as a large triangle OAB with a smaller triangle PQB taken from it. You could alternatively look at the shape OAQP as a rectangle with two triangles added.

(b) When hung from point P, the lamina will lie with its centre of mass vertically below the point of suspension (i.e. P). This means that line PM will be vertical. Hence angle between PM and PQ will be the angle marked θ in the diagram below.

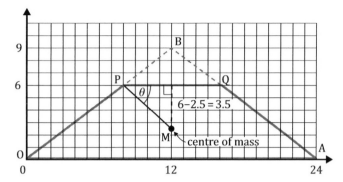

$$\tan \theta = \frac{3.5}{4}$$

Hence $\theta = 41.2°$

Summary: Statics

Resolution of forces

Replacing a single force with two forces acting at right angles

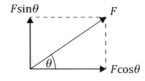

Force F can be replaced by two components at right angles to each other:

A horizontal component $F\cos\theta$

A vertical component $F\sin\theta$

Replacing two forces acting at right angles with a single force

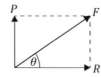

Using Pythagoras' theorem, so we obtain $F^2 = P^2 + R^2$

Hence $F = \sqrt{P^2 + R^2}$ and angle to the horizontal, $\theta = \tan^{-1}\left(\dfrac{P}{R}\right)$

The moment of a force about a point

Moment = Force × distance

The unit of moment is the newton metre (N m) and the distance must be the perpendicular distance from the point about which moments are taken to the line of action of the force. Moments have a sense/direction (i.e. clockwise or anticlockwise).

The principle of moments:

When a body is in equilibrium, the sum of the clockwise moments is equal to the sum of the anticlockwise moments.

Equilibrium of a rigid body under the action of parallel coplanar forces

If a rigid body, such as a rod, under the action of parallel coplanar forces is in equilibrium then the following is true:

1. The resultant force in any direction is zero.

2. The sum of the moments about any point is zero.

Centre of mass of uniform laminae (triangles, rectangles, circles and composite shapes)

Centre of mass of a rectangle – situated where the lines joining the mid-points of the sides intersect.

Centre of mass of a circle – situated at the centre of the circle.

Centre of mass of a triangle – situated on the median (i.e. a line joining the vertex of the triangle to the mid-point of the base).

The following formula is used to work out where the mid-point lies on the median:

Centre of mass for a triangular lamina is $\frac{2}{3}$ along median from vertex.

For a right-angled triangle the centre of mass is one-third of the way out from the right angle along both sides, or two-thirds from a vertex towards the right angle.

Test yourself answers

Topic 1 Rectilinear motion

① (a)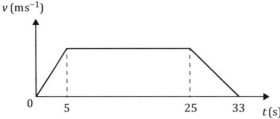

(b) $u = 0, a = 0.9, t = 5, v = ?$

Using $v = u + at$

gives $v = 0 + (0.9 \times 5) = 4.5 \text{ m s}^{-1}$

(c) Acceleration = Gradient of the graph between $t = 25$ and $t = 33$ s.

$$= \frac{0 - 4.5}{33 - 25} = -0.56 \text{ m s}^{-2}$$

Hence deceleration = 0.56 m s^{-2}

> Note that if you say that this is a deceleration, then you need to remove the minus sign.

(d) Distance travelled = area under the velocity–time graph

$$= \tfrac{1}{2}(20 + 33) \times 4.5 = 119.25 \text{ m}$$

② (a) Taking the upward velocity as positive, we have

$u = 20, v = 0, a = -g = -9.8$

Using $v^2 = u^2 + 2as$ gives $0 = 20^2 + (2 \times (-9.8) \times s)$

Solving for s, gives $s = 20.4 \text{ m}$

(b) Using $s = ut + \tfrac{1}{2}at^2$

$$0 = 20t + \left(\tfrac{1}{2} \times (-9.8) \times t^2\right)$$

$$0 = 20t - 4.9t^2$$

$$0 = t(20 - 4.9t)$$

$$t = 0 \text{ or } 4.1 \text{ s}$$

> The displacement, s, is zero when the stone returns to its point of projection.

Hence time = 4.1 s

> $t = 0$ is ignored as a possible time as this is the time of projection.

③ (a) Taking the downward direction as positive.

$u = 0.8, t = 3.5, a = g = 9.8, v = ?$

Using $v = u + at$ we have $v = 0.8 + (9.8 \times 3.5) = 35.1 \text{ m s}^{-1}$

(b) Using $s = ut + \tfrac{1}{2}at^2 = (0.8 \times 3.5) + \left(\tfrac{1}{2} \times 9.8 \times 3.5^2\right) = 62.8 \text{ m}$

④ (a) Taking upwards as the positive direction, we have

$u = 15, a = -g = -9.8, v = 0$

Using $v = u + at$ gives

$0 = 15 - 9.8t$ 　　　　　　Hence $t = 1.53$ s

(b) Using $v^2 = u^2 + 2as$ gives

$0 = 15^2 + (2 \times (-9.8)s)$ 　　Hence $s = 11.48$ m

Topic 2 Dynamics of a particle

①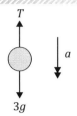

We can ignore the weight of a light string but not the weight of a heavy chain.

The weight of the particle acts vertically down and is given by $W = mg$. As the mass here is 3 kg, W = 3g.

There is no resultant force in the horizontal direction.

Applying Newton's second law in the vertical direction gives

$ma = 3g - T$

$3 \times 2 = (3 \times 9.8) - T$

giving $T = 23.4$ N

② (a)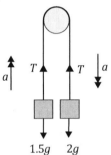

Applying Newton's second law of motion to the 1.5 kg mass, we obtain

$ma = T - 1.5g$

$1.5a = T - 1.5g$ (1)

Applying Newton's second law of motion to the 2 kg mass, we obtain

$ma = 2g - T$

$2a = 2g - T$ (2)

Solving equations (1) and (2) simultaneously, we obtain

$T = 16.8$ N

(b) Solving equations (1) and (2) simultaneously, we obtain

$a = 1.4$ m s^{-2}

(c) When both particles are 1 m apart, the 1.5 kg mass would have risen by 0.5 m and the 2 kg mass would have fallen by 0.5 m.

For the 2 kg mass, $u = 0$, $a = 1.4$, $s = 0.5$, $v = ?$

Using $v^2 = u^2 + 2as$,

$v^2 = 0^2 + 2 \times 1.4 \times 0.5$

Hence $v = 1.18$ m s^{-1}

Use the equations of motion to find the final velocity, v.

Remember that the equations of motion are not in the formula booklet and must therefore be memorised.

③ (a)

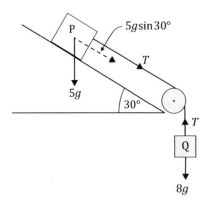

> The component of the weight is $5g \sin 30°$ acting down the slope.

> The acceleration of the block will act down the slope.

Applying Newton's second law of motion to particle P, we obtain

$$ma = T + 5g \sin 30°$$
$$5a = T + 2.5g \tag{1}$$

Applying Newton's second law of motion to particle Q, we obtain

$$8a = 8g - T \tag{2}$$

Adding equations (1) and (2), we obtain

$$13a = 10.5g$$
$$a = 7.9 \text{ m s}^{-2}$$

(b) Substituting $a = 7.9$ into equation (1), we obtain

$$5 \times 7.9 = T + (2.5 \times 9.8)$$
$$T = 15.1 \text{ N (correct to 1 decimal place)}$$

④ (a)

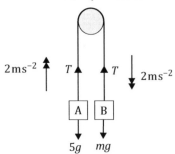

Applying Newton's second law to particle A, we obtain

$$5a = T - 5g$$
$$10 = T - (5 \times 9.8)$$
$$T = 59 \text{ N}$$

(b) Applying Newton's second law to particle B, we obtain

$$m \times 2 = mg - T$$
$$2m = mg - T$$
$$2m = 9.8m - 59$$
$$m = 7.6 \text{ kg}$$

Topic 3 Friction

① (a)

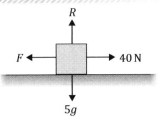

(b) Resolving vertically, we obtain $R = 5g = 5 \times 9.8 = 49$ N

(c) Applying Newton's second law to the horizontal motion, we obtain

$$ma = 40 - F$$

$$5 \times 2 = 40 - F$$

Hence $F = 30$ N

② (a)

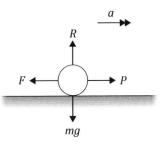

Resolving vertically, we have

$$R = 3g$$

$$= 3 \times 9.8$$

$$= 29.4 \text{ N}$$

$$F_{MAX} = \mu R = 0.3 \times 29.4 = 8.82 \text{ N}$$

Remember to take g as 9.8 m s^{-2}.

As the maximum frictional force (i.e. 8.82 N) is larger than the applied force P of 8 N, the frictional force F will balance P. Hence $F = 8$ N.

F_{MAX} is the limiting friction. This is the maximum friction before movement occurs.

As P and F are balanced, there is no resultant force so the acceleration will be 0 m s^{-2} so the particle will remain at rest.

(b) $R = 29.4$ N and $F_{MAX} = 8.82$ N

P is greater than F_{MAX} so there will be a resultant force.

Resultant force = $P - F_{MAX} = 12 - 8.82 = 3.18$ N

Applying Newton's second law, we obtain

$$ma = 3.18$$

$$3a = 3.18$$

Hence $a = 1.06 \text{ m s}^{-2}$

③ (a)

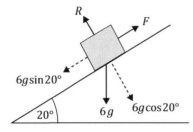

Resolving at right angles to the plane, we have
$$R = 6g \cos 20° = 6 \times 9.8 \times \cos 20° = 55.25 \text{ N}$$

For limiting friction, $F = 6g \sin 20° = 20.11$ N

On the point of slipping, limiting friction $F = \mu R$

Hence least value of μ is $\mu = \dfrac{F}{R} = \dfrac{20.11}{55.25} = 0.36$ (correct to 2 significant figures)

(b) For motion down the plane, $ma = 6g \sin 20° - F$

so
$$6a = 20.11 - (0.2 \times 6g \cos 20°)$$
$$6a = 20.11 - (0.2 \times 55.25)$$

so
$$a = 1.51 \text{ m s}^{-2}$$

Grade boost

Always check to see if the question asks for the answer to be given to a certain number of significant figures or decimal places. Failure to do this may cost you marks.

Topic 4 Momentum and impulse

①

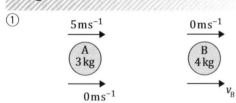

Applying conservation of momentum, we obtain
$$(3 \times 5) + (4 \times 0) = (3 \times 0) + 4v_B$$

Hence $v_B = 3.75$ m s^{-1}

② (a)

Applying conservation of momentum, we obtain
$$(0.2 \times 0.1) + (0.1 \times 0.05) = (0.2 \times 0.08) + 0.1v_B$$

Solving, we obtain $v_B = 0.09$ m s^{-1}

(b) Coefficient of restitution, $-e = \dfrac{v_B - v_A}{u_B - u_A}$

$$-e = \dfrac{0.09 - 0.08}{0.05 - 0.1} = -0.2$$

Hence coefficient of restitution, $e = 0.2$

③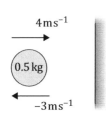

Impulse, I = change in momentum

$\qquad = m(v - u)$

$\qquad = 0.5(-3 - 4) = -3.5 \, \text{N s}$

Hence impulse exerted on the wall by the ball = 3.5 N s

> Here we have taken the initial velocity as being positive so the rebound velocity will be negative.

④ (a)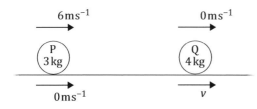

> Note that this impulse is the impulse exerted by the wall on the ball. According to Newton's third law there will be an equal and opposite reaction to this. This means that the magnitude of the impulse exerted on the wall by the ball is 3.5 N s.

Applying conservation of momentum, we obtain

$\qquad (3 \times 6) + (4 \times 0) = (3 \times 0) + 4v$

Hence $\qquad\qquad v = 4.5 \, \text{m s}^{-1}$

(b) Using $\dfrac{v_Q - v_P}{u_Q - u_P} = -e = \dfrac{4.5 - 0}{0 - 6} = -0.75$

Hence coefficient of restitution, $e = 0.75$

Topic 5 Statics

①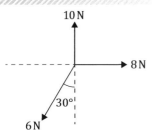

Component of the 6 N force in the horizontal direction = 6 sin 30° = 3 N (to the left)

Resolving horizontally we obtain, net resultant force = 8 − 3 = 5 N (to the right)

Component of the 6 N force in the vertical direction = 6 cos 30° = 5.1962 N (downwards)

Resolving vertically, we obtain, net resultant force = 10 − 5.1962 = 4.8038 N (upwards)

Resultant force R is found using Pythagoras' theorem

$$R^2 = 5^2 + 4.8038^2$$

giving $\quad R = 6.9337\,N$

$$\theta = \tan^{-1}\left(\frac{4.8038}{5}\right) = 43.9° \text{ (to the direction of the 8 N force)}$$

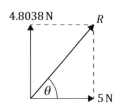

②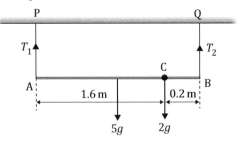

Resolving vertically, we obtain

$$R_1 + R_2 = 0.5g + 4g$$

$$R_1 + R_2 = 4.5 \times 9.8$$

$$R_1 + R_2 = 44.1\,N \tag{1}$$

Clockwise moments = anticlockwise moments.

Taking moments about P, we obtain

$$4g \times 0.6 = (0.5g \times 0.4) + (R_2 \times 1)$$

Hence $\quad R_2 = 21.56\,N$

Substituting $R_2 = 21.56$ into equation (1) we obtain

$$R_1 + 21.56 = 44.1$$

Hence $\quad R_1 = 22.54\,N$

③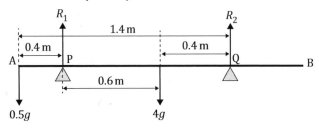

As the rod is in equilibrium, resolving vertically, we obtain

$$T_1 + T_2 = 5g + 2g$$

$$T_1 + T_2 = 7g \tag{1}$$

Taking moments about point A we obtain

$$(5g \times 0.9) + (2g \times 1.6) = T_2 \times 1.8$$

Solving, gives $\qquad T_2 = 41.9222\,N \qquad T_2 = 41.9\,N$ (correct to one decimal place)

Substituting this value for T_2 into equation (1), we obtain

$$T_1 + 41.9222 = 7 \times 9.8$$

$$T_1 = 26.6778\,N \qquad T_1 = 26.7\,N \text{ (correct to one decimal place)}$$